ZB Zaner-Bloser
A Highlights Company

Grade Level Consultants

Margaret Bateman
Montgomery, Alabama

Cindy Daniel
Bothell, Washington

Suzanne Klein
Hilliard, Ohio

Nancy Morgan
Sharon, Pennsylvania

Joan Pawloski
Grand Rapids, Michigan

Illustration: Steve Botts, Tracy Greenwalt

ISBN: 978-1-4531-1209-0

This book is printed on paper certified by third-party standards for sustainably managed forestry.

Zaner-Bloser, Inc.
800.421.3018
zaner-bloser.com

Printed in the United States of America
5 6 7 8 9 10 11 12 13 14 27950 22 21 20 19 18 ZB Code 16

Table of Contents

Unit 1 Sentence Structure

The World Outside: Water

Unit 2 Parts of Speech

Looking Back: United States History

Unit 3 Usage

Unforgettable Folks: Athletes

Unit 4 Grammar

Grab Bag: Cars

Unit 5 Mechanics

Beasts & Critters: Amphibians and Reptiles

Appendix

Unit Pretests

Extra Practice

Unit Posttests

Water / covers most of Earth's surface.
a b

Which part (a or b) of this sentence tells whom or what the sentence is about? ___ Which part (a or b) tells what happens? ___

Every sentence has a subject and a predicate. The **complete subject** is made up of a noun or pronoun and words that tell about it. The subject tells whom or what the sentence is about. The **complete predicate** is made up of a verb and words that tell what the subject is, has, or does.

See Handbook Sections 10 and 11

Practice

Underline the complete subject once. Underline the complete predicate twice.

1. The human body is about two-thirds water.
2. A typical American uses almost 100 gallons of water every day.
3. An adult needs about 2½ quarts of water each day.
4. This water comes from food and beverages.
5. A 15-minute shower uses about 75 gallons of water.
6. Many different industries use water.
7. Gasoline production requires water.
8. Agriculture needs large quantities of water, too.
9. The cultivation of wheat for one loaf of bread requires 150 gallons of water.
10. Some farmers use water-saving techniques.
11. The world's oceans contain salt water.
12. Special treatment plants can remove the salt from the water.

Drinking water is tested regularly throughout the United States.

Name ______________________________

Apply

Create a sentence from each phrase. Add either a subject or a predicate. Underline the complete subject in your sentence.

13. a thirsty person ______________________________

____

14. a cold, clear stream ______________________________

____

15. must be watered often ______________________________

____

16. uses large quantities of water ______________________________

____

17. rain and snow ______________________________

____

Reinforce

Write three sentences about your favorite water activity, such as swimming, fishing, boating, or wakeboarding. Circle each complete subject and underline each complete predicate.

18. ______________________________

____

19. ______________________________

____

20. ______________________________

____

Read and Analyze

Simple Subjects and Simple Predicates

Heat changes the water in the kettle from a liquid into a gas.
The steam from the kettle rises toward the ceiling.

The complete subject in each sentence is in boldfaced type. Circle the most important word in each complete subject. Underline the verb in each sentence that tells what the subject does.

The **simple subject** is the most important word or words in the complete subject. It is a noun or pronoun and tells whom or what the sentence is about. The **simple predicate** is the most important word or words in the complete predicate. It is a verb. The simple predicate may tell what the subject did or what was done to the subject. It may also be a form of the verb *be*.

See Handbook Sections 10 and 11

Practice

Circle the simple subject in each sentence. Draw a line under the simple predicate.

1. Water occurs as a liquid, a solid, and a gas.
2. Steam is a gaseous form of water.
3. Solid forms of water include ice and snow.
4. No other substance on Earth exists in all three forms.
5. Rain replenishes Earth's water supply.
6. Moisture evaporates from Earth's surface.
7. Vapor collects in the clouds.
8. One cloud contains billions of water molecules.
9. The molecules inside the cloud grow heavy.
10. Water returns to Earth in the form of rain or snow.
11. All animals and plants need water.
12. Some desert creatures get water from plants.

Water is the only substance on Earth that is present in three forms: solid, liquid, and gas.

Name ______________________________

Apply

Write five sentences about water in its solid state. You may use nouns and verbs from the word bank as simple subjects and simple predicates.

hailstones	glisten	snowball	glacier	crashes
icicles	iceberg	melts	whizzes	clatter

13. ______________________________

____

14. ______________________________

____

15. ______________________________

____

16. ______________________________

____

17. ______________________________

____

Reinforce

See Handbook Section 32

Ask an adult to help you search the Internet for information about winter weather in your area. Then write a brief paragraph describing winter weather where you live. Underline each simple subject in red. Underline each simple predicate in blue.

____

____

____

____

____

____

_____ Tides in the ocean rise and fall regularly each day.
_____ The sun and the moon cause the tides.

Write *S* next to the sentence with two or more subjects. Write *P* next to the sentence with two or more verbs.

A **compound subject** is two or more subjects joined by the conjunction *and* or *or*. A **compound predicate** is two or more verbs joined by a conjunction.

See Handbook Sections 10 and 11

Practice

Circle the two simple subjects that make up each compound subject. Underline the two verbs that make up each compound predicate.

1. Ports and harbors are helped by tides in many ways.
2. Tides clean the channels and keep them deep enough for ships.
3. Ocean liners and cargo ships sail through channels at high tide.
4. A high tide can lift a large ship and guide it into port.
5. Tides pick up waste from the shore and carry it far out to the bottom of the sea.
6. Fishing crews and sailors pay close attention to the tides in their area.
7. The new moon and the full moon bring spring tides, the highest and lowest tides of each month.
8. Long ago sailors observed the moon and used a compass.
9. Today fishing boat crews and ship captains rely on the Internet for information on tides.
10. Tide charts and weather reports help navigators.

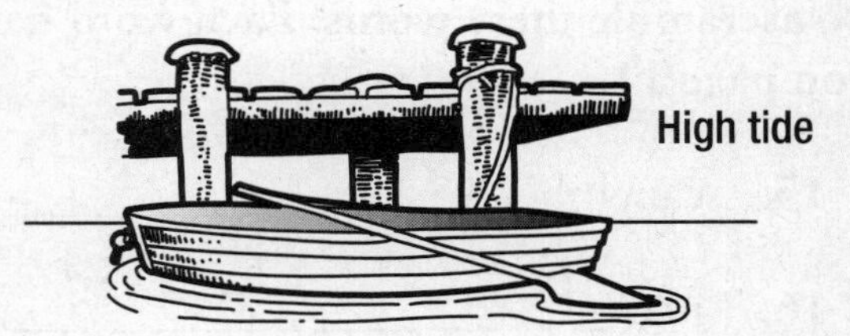

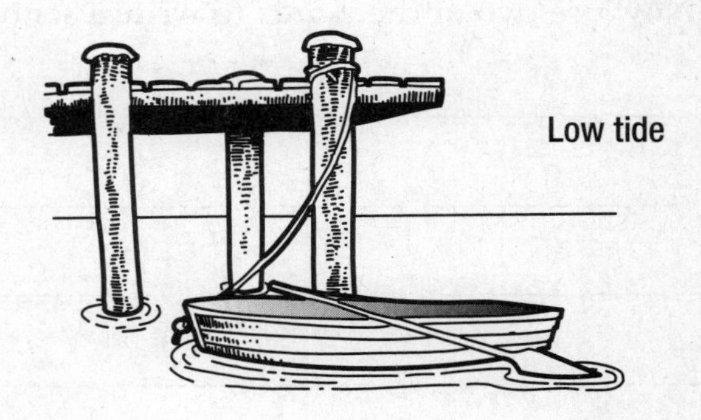

Name ______________________________

Apply

Combine each pair of sentences to form one sentence that has either a compound subject or a compound predicate.

11. Visitors to the beach can swim at high tide. They can dig clams at low tide.

____

____

12. Sea stars are often left high and dry at low tide. So are sea anemones.

____

____

13. Tides contain energy. Waves contain energy, too. ______________________________

____

14. Underwater machines harness tidal power. They convert it into valuable energy.

____

____

Reinforce

Unscramble these words. Each word names something found in harbors. All of the words appear on page 11.

15. scanelnh ______________

16. sited ______________

17. rostp ______________

18. iorslas ______________

Now use two of the words to write a sentence with a compound subject or a compound predicate.

____

____

____

____

Read and Analyze

Direct Objects

The **oceans** of **Earth** contain many **plants** and **fish**.

Circle the boldfaced nouns that tell what the oceans contain.

The **direct object** is the noun or pronoun that receives the action of the verb. Only action verbs can take a direct object. A **compound direct object** occurs when more than one noun or pronoun receives the action of the verb. To find the direct object, say the verb, and then ask "What?" or "Whom?" For example, to find the direct object of *The oceans of Earth contain many plants and fish*, ask "Contain what?" The answer is "plants and fish."

See Handbook Section 20

Practice

Circle the direct object or compound direct object in each sentence.

1. We use the ocean for many purposes.
2. Divers explore its colorful reefs.
3. Diners eat its fish.
4. Surfers ride its wild waves.
5. Workers take minerals, pearls, sponges, and salt from it.
6. Boats harvest seaweed from the ocean.
7. Manufacturers make medicines, ice cream, and cosmetics from seaweed.
8. Container ships use the oceans as superhighways.

Coral reefs are home to many colorful species of fish.

9. Luxury liners use the oceans as a vast playground.
10. Water purification plants turn seawater into drinking water for our thirsty planet.

Name ______________________________

Apply

Write a direct object or a compound direct object after each action verb. Use words from the word bank and your own words.

treasures	clouds	ocean	pictures	creatures	plants	rain	coral

11. People mine the rich ______________________ for valuable minerals.
12. Divers gather precious ______________________ from the ocean bottom.
13. Photographers take beautiful ______________________ of colorful fish.
14. Scientists study strange ______________________ in the ocean's depths.
15. Moisture from the ocean forms ______________________.
16. These clouds eventually bring ______________________ to our mountains and valleys.

Reinforce

Draw an underwater scene below or use a computer graphics program to create such a scene. You can use the action words and direct objects in the word bank for ideas. Then write two sentences describing your scene.

sank	gave	reef	octopus	found	made	fins	cave

17. ____

____

18. ____

____

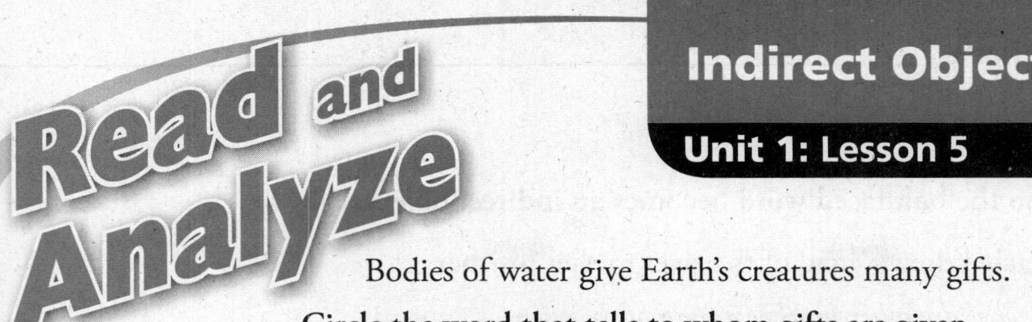

Bodies of water give Earth's creatures many gifts.

Circle the word that tells to whom gifts are given.

An **indirect object** is a noun or pronoun that comes before a direct object. The indirect object tells to whom something has been given, told, or taught. Indirect objects appear only in sentences with direct objects. To test whether a noun or pronoun is an indirect object, try moving it after the direct object and putting the word *to* or *for* in front of it: *Bodies of water give many gifts to Earth's creatures.*

See Handbook Section 20

Practice

The direct object in each sentence is in boldfaced type. Circle each indirect object.

1. Potholes offer migrating ducks resting **places**.
2. Estuaries give shellfish a peaceful **habitat**.
3. Bayous offer alligators many hiding **places**.
4. Ponds give frogs a wet, wonderful **home**.
5. Flooding rivers bring farmers rich **silt** for their fields.
6. Rivers also give spawning salmon a **nursery** for their young.
7. Hot springs offer people with sore muscles **relief** from pain.
8. Creeks offer hikers a pleasant, warbling **song**.
9. Waterfalls give photographers a magnificent **subject** for a picture.
10. Oceans send the skies **water vapor** that eventually returns to Earth as precipitation.
11. Bays provide boats a safe **haven** in stormy weather.
12. Sweetwater springs give hikers lifesaving drinking **water**.
13. Underground aquifers give farmers **water** for irrigation.
14. Lakes offer boaters a **place** to have fun.

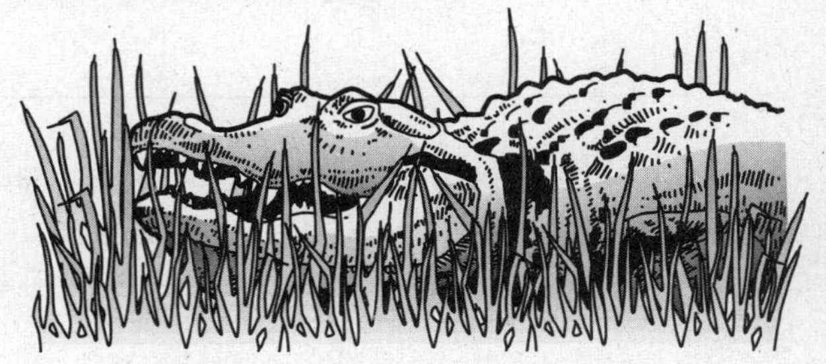

Alligators move slowly through the shallow, stagnant waters of the bayous.

Name ______________________________

Apply

Rewrite each sentence so the boldfaced word becomes an indirect object.

Example Rachel drew a map of the river for her **brother.**

Rachel drew her brother a map of the river.

15. Eddie sold his kayak to **Rachel.** ______________________________

____

16. Eddie gave two life jackets to **Benvi.** ______________________________

____

17. Hobie sang a sea song to the **crew.** ______________________________

____

18. Ernesto wrote a letter about his canoe trip to **Maia.** ______________________________

____

19. Chul told a story about his days as a sailor to **Dexter.** ______________________________

____

Reinforce

Imagine you and three friends are planning a canoe trip. Write three sentences with indirect objects. Each sentence should tell to whom you will give each item in the word bank.

first-aid kit	camera	portable stove

20. ______________________________

____

21. ______________________________

____

22. ______________________________

____

Predicate Nouns and Predicate Adjectives

Unit 1: Lesson 6

Read and Analyze

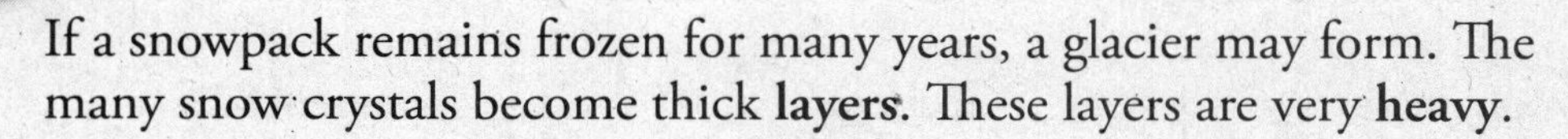

If a snowpack remains frozen for many years, a glacier may form. The many snow crystals become thick **layers**. These layers are very **heavy**.

Circle the boldfaced noun that tells what the subject is or becomes. Underline the boldfaced adjective that describes the subject.

A **linking verb** connects the subject of a sentence to a word or phrase in the predicate that tells about the subject. A **predicate noun** follows a linking verb and renames the subject. A **predicate adjective** follows a linking verb and describes the subject.

See Handbook Section 11

Practice

Draw one line under each boldfaced word that is a predicate noun. Draw two lines under each boldfaced word that is a predicate adjective. Circle the linking verb in each sentence.

1. The layers become a **mass** of solid ice.
2. A mass of solid ice is a **glacier**.
3. Continental glaciers and valley glaciers are two **types** of glaciers.
4. Continental glaciers are **sheets** of thick ice.
5. Valley glaciers are **long** and **thin**.
6. Alaska's Glacier Bay National Park is **home** to bears, wolves, and mountain goats.
7. A glacier's movement is quite **slow**.
8. A glacier's surface is its hardest **part**.
9. Mountain climbers become extremely **cautious** on glaciers.
10. The crevasses in a glacier's surface are **dangerous**.
11. Crevasses are deep **cracks** in the ice.

Mountain climbers use special equipment to scale glaciers.

Name ______________________________

Apply

Write a predicate noun or a predicate adjective to complete each sentence. You may use words from the word bank if you wish. Use an article (*a, an,* or *the*) if it is needed.

obstacle	iceberg	essential	cause
visible	disastrous	shock	ocean liner

12. A floating chunk of ice from a glacier becomes ____________________.

13. Only the very tip of an iceberg is ____________________.

14. A collision between a passenger ship and an iceberg can be ____________________.

15. A life vest for every passenger on board a ship is ____________________.

16. The *Titanic* was a large ____________________ that sank in 1912.

17. An iceberg was ____________________ of its destruction.

18. The sinking of the "unsinkable" *Titanic* was ____________________ to the world.

Reinforce

See Handbook Sections 31 and 32

Out of 2,200 passengers aboard the *Titanic,* only 705 were rescued. Ask an adult to help you find an article in an online encyclopedia about the sinking of the *Titanic.* Then imagine that you are interviewing a survivor. Write a question and an answer for a "news flash" of April 15, 1912. Use at least one predicate noun or predicate adjective to complete each item.

19. Question: ____

____

____

____

20. Answer: ____

____

____

____

Read and Analyze

A large lake can affect the weather in nearby areas.

Which words tell where the weather is affected?

____

A **prepositional phrase** can tell *how, what kind, when, how much,* or *where*. A prepositional phrase begins with a **preposition**, such as *in, over, of, to,* or *by*. It ends with a noun or pronoun that is the **object of the preposition**. Words between the preposition and the object of the preposition are also part of the prepositional phrase. A prepositional phrase can appear at the beginning, middle, or end of a sentence.

See Handbook Section 19

Practice

Underline each prepositional phrase. Circle the preposition that begins the phrase.

1. A lake absorbs heat during the summer.
2. It releases this heat slowly over the following months.
3. A lake warms cold winds in cooler months.
4. The winds off the lake are relatively warm.
5. These temperate winds can extend the growing season of an area.
6. The Great Lakes are important to Michigan's fruit crops.
7. The lakes help keep the air around the orchards warm.
8. Michigan cherries are shipped to many American cities.
9. The cherries are harvested before the winter frost.
10. Much produce is shipped by train.

The Great Lakes and the waterways that connect them are vital to the economies of the United States and Canada.

Name ______________________________

Apply

Add a prepositional phrase or two to each sentence. Then rewrite each sentence. You may use phrases from the word bank or think of your own.

without their water	to cities and towns	for recreation
during summer months	for irrigation	for manufacturing

11. Lakes are important. ______________________________

____

12. People use them. ______________________________

____

13. Industries use their water. ______________________________

____

14. Farmers use their water. ______________________________

____

Reinforce

Use the clues to complete the puzzle. Each answer is a preposition.

Across

3. My family visits Lake Michigan __ the summer months.
4. We drive __ the state of Michigan.
6. I enjoy going __ the lake.
8. It takes several days to drive __ the entire lake.
9. The lake reflects the color of the sky __ it.

Down

1. We swim in the lake __ July and August.
2. I wear goggles when I swim __ the water.
4. I don't like it when fish swim __ me.
5. We pass factories and orchards __ our journey.
7. I like diving __ the cool water.
10. Once I saw a fish swim __ me.

Simple and Compound Sentences

Unit 1: Lesson 8

a. For a hundred years people dreamed of a waterway between the Great Lakes **and** the Atlantic Ocean.
b. De Witt Clinton planned a canal, **but** people sneered at his idea.

Cross out the boldfaced conjunction in each sentence.

Which sentence could become two separate sentences? ________

A **compound sentence** is two or more closely related simple sentences. A **simple sentence** is also called an independent clause. The two clauses can be joined by a comma and a conjunction (*and, but, or*) or by a semicolon (;).

See Handbook Sections 8, 12, and 21

Practice

Write *S* next to each simple sentence and *C* next to each compound sentence. Circle the conjunction or semicolon in each compound sentence.

A lock allows a ship to pass from one body of water to another.

1. The federal government would not give Clinton any money for his canal, but he did not give up. _____
2. Clinton asked the New York legislature for money, and the State of New York agreed to his request. _____
3. The governor of New York named Clinton the head of the canal commission in 1816; Clinton became governor of New York the next year. _____
4. His crew began construction on July 4, 1817. _____
5. The Erie Canal grew, and the towns along its course became busier. _____
6. The canal was not completed until 1825. _____
7. Now raw materials from the Great Lakes region could be shipped to the East, and manufactured goods from Eastern cities could be shipped to the upper Midwest. _____
8. The canal cost over seven million dollars, but tolls earned 17 times that by 1882. _____
9. Early opponents feared the canal would never pay for itself; they were proven wrong. _____

Name ______________________________

Apply

Rewrite each pair of simple sentences as one compound sentence.

10. The *Seneca Chief* made the first journey through the Erie Canal in ten days. De Witt Clinton was one of the happy passengers.

____

____

11. The Erie Canal cost more than seven million dollars. It proved to be a good investment.

____

____

12. Barges moved slowly along the canal. They carried heavy loads cheaply and dependably.

____

____

Reinforce

Many canals have locks to raise and lower boats. The diagram on page 21 shows what happens when a boat passes through a lock. Put the independent clauses below in order to tell what is happening in the diagram. Then combine the clauses to form three compound sentences.

The lock is opened a second time.	The lock is opened for the first time.
The water in the lock rises.	The ship enters the lock.
The ship sails out of the lock.	The ship sails up to the lock.

13. ______________________________

____

14. ______________________________

____

15. ______________________________

____

Read and Analyze

Dependent and Independent Clauses

As the wind pushes against the water, the wind creates waves.

Look at the two parts of this sentence. Which part makes sense by itself?

a. the boldfaced part **b.** the underlined part

An **independent clause** is a sentence that makes sense by itself. A **dependent clause** has a subject and a verb, but it does not make complete sense by itself. It needs—or is dependent on—an independent clause. A dependent clause often begins with a word such as *although, because, if, as,* or *when.*

See Handbook Sections 12 and 21

Practice

Draw one line under each independent clause. Draw two lines under each dependent clause. Circle the word that begins each dependent clause.

1. Although some people think waves are caused by tides, the wind causes most waves.
2. When the wind blows for a long time at great speed, the waves grow larger.
3. Because waves keep moving even after the winds stop, some waves travel far from where they began.
4. Although storms often produce gigantic waves, few huge waves have ever been measured precisely.
5. When a ship is in the middle of a storm, its crew members must focus on survival.

The power and repetition of waves can carve steep cliffs.

6. Navigating a ship through a storm is still extremely difficult, though modern tracking equipment does provide some help.
7. If the crew members are careless, they may be washed overboard by a large wave.
8. A sailor aboard *USS Ramapo* measured a 112-foot wave when the ship was caught in a hurricane in 1933.
9. As *Weather Reporter* sailed the Atlantic in 1972, its instruments recorded an 86-foot wave.
10. By the time they reach the shore, most waves have traveled for many miles.

Name ______________________________

Apply

Draw a line to match each dependent clause on the left with an independent clause on the right. Then write the new sentences you created. Be sure to add a comma in between clauses.

Because waves often hurl 100-pound rocks at it	A giant tsunami hit Waipi'o Valley on the big island of Hawaii.
Although most waves are harmless	Many lives were lost.
When an earthquake struck in Alaska in 1946	Tillamook Lighthouse in Oregon has steel bars built around it.
Because people had no warning	Some huge waves cause damage.

11. ______________________________

____

12. ______________________________

____

13. ______________________________

____

14. ______________________________

____

Reinforce

Wave warnings often appear near beaches where rough surf is common. Add an independent clause to each dependent clause below to create sentences that warn people of the danger.

when you walk on the beach	if you use caution

15. ______________________________

____

16. ______________________________

____

Wherever big waves regularly form,
you will find big wave surfers in search of a thrilling ride.

Circle the part of the sentence that makes sense by itself.

An **independent clause** has a subject and a verb, and makes sense by itself. A **dependent clause** has a subject and a verb, but it does not make complete sense by itself. Many dependent clauses begin with *although, because, if, when,* or *after*. A **complex sentence** is made up of a dependent clause and an independent clause.

See Handbook Sections 12 and 21

Practice

Write *CX* next to each complex sentence.

1. The native people of Hawaii have ridden waves on boards for hundreds of years. ________
2. In the late 1940s and early 1950s, some surfers gathered at Makaha, where giant waves form in fall and winter. ________
3. Makaha is on the west shore of Oahu, the most populous island in Hawaii. ________
4. When the waves at Makaha grew large, those big wave pioneers paddled out to the break line. ________
5. Although they frequently were tossed around or pulled under by the powerful waves, these surfers learned the secrets of big wave riding. ________
6. When George Downing developed a special big wave surfboard, it made the rides easier. ________
7. In the 1970s Eddie Aikau became the star of big-wave surfing because he was fearless and very skillful. ________
8. Hawaii offers five of the best spots for big wave surfing, but there are also famous places in northern California, Mexico, Brazil, Chile, and South Africa. ________
9. If you watch big wave surf events today, you may see Maya Gabeira astride a huge breaker. ________
10. In 2009 she won the ESPY Award for Female Sports Athlete of the Year. ________

Eddie Aikau is one of the most famous surfers to come from the state of Hawaii.

Name ______________________________

Apply

Draw a line to match each clause on the left with a clause on the right. Write the new sentences on the lines. Use commas where needed.

When surfers get tossed off a big wave	they may run short of oxygen
Because they have been spun around and pushed so far down	they may be pushed 40 feet under the surface
Unless they swim upward immediately	they at first cannot tell up from down
If surfers take too long on the way up to the surface	they may get pushed back under by the next wave

11. ______________________________

____

12. ______________________________

____

13. ______________________________

____

14. ______________________________

____

Reinforce

Write a paragraph about an exciting sport. Include at least one complex sentence in your paragraph.

____

____

____

____

____

____

____

____

Relative Pronouns and Relative Adverbs

Unit 1: Lesson 11

Read and Analyze

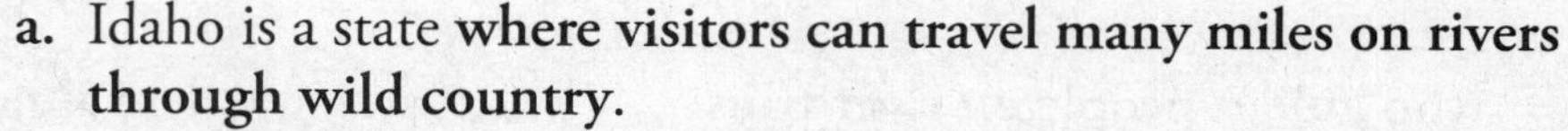

a. Idaho is a state **where visitors can travel many miles on rivers through wild country.**

b. Captain Elmer Earl is a jet boat pilot **who has taken thousands of people on rides up the Snake River.**

Which sentence has a boldfaced clause that describes a person? _____ Circle the first word in this clause. Which sentence has a boldfaced clause that tells more about a time, a place, or a reason? _____ Circle the first word in this clause.

When the pronoun *who, whom, whose, which,* or *that* begins a dependent clause that describes a person, place, or thing, it is called a **relative pronoun**. When the word *when, where,* or *why* begins a dependent clause that tells about a time, a place, or a reason, it is called a **relative adverb**.

See Handbook Sections 16 and 18

Practice

Circle the first word in each boldfaced dependent clause. Write *RP* if it is a relative pronoun. Write *RA* if it is a relative adverb.

1. Elmer Earl's grandparents settled in a place at the bottom of a steep canyon **where a small creek flows into the Snake River.** ________
2. The Nez Perce Indians, **who have lived in the area around the mouth of the Snake River for generations**, were their neighbors. ________
3. Only a handful of people live along the long, narrow channel **that the Snake River carved for itself.** ________
4. In fact, the Snake flows for 100 miles through the deepest, narrowest gorge in North America before it reaches the spot **where it empties into the Columbia River.** ________
5. During the years **when Elmer Earl piloted a boat up the Snake River**, he delivered supplies and mail to the remote ranches in the canyon. ________
6. He brought the wool **that the ranchers produced** back to the towns near the mouth of the Snake. ________
7. No roads will ever reach into the steep, rocky region **where Elmer Earl piloted his boat.** ________
8. Jet boat passengers see the same kinds of wildlife **that Meriwether Lewis, William Clark, and Sacagawea saw two hundred years ago.** ________
9. The Luna House Museum in Lewiston, Idaho, displays artifacts from the days **when trappers hunted for beaver in the area.** ________
10. Toni Earl, Elmer's wife, was one of the people **who founded this local museum.** ________

Name ______________________________

Apply

Complete each sentence with the appropriate dependent clause. Then circle the relative pronouns and underline the relative adverbs in the sentences.

who guides people on river trips	where almost no one lives
which is the West's wildest river	when the snow melts

11. We will visit Stanley, Idaho, in the month ______________________________
12. There we will meet our cousin, ______________________________
13. We will kayak with him on the Salmon River, ______________________________ ______________________________
14. We will spend a week in an area ______________________________

Reinforce

Unscramble the six words below. Circle the three words that can be used as relative pronouns. Underline the three words that can be used as relative adverbs.

15. ohw ______________
16. newh ______________
17. hewer ______________
18. hatt ______________
19. hyw ______________
20. chihw ______________

Now use three of the words to write three sentences about a river located in or near your community.

____

____

____

____

____

____

a. *Tsunami* is a Japanese word meaning "port wave."
b. A huge wave with enormous power.
c. If people are not warned beforehand.
d. Tsunamis should not be called tidal waves, they are not caused by tides.

Which item is a correct sentence? ________

Which item has no verb? ________

Which item is a dependent clause? ________

Which item is made up of two independent clauses without a conjunction? ________

A **fragment** does not tell a complete thought. A **run-on sentence** is a compound sentence that is missing a comma and a conjunction. A **comma splice** is a run-on sentence that has a comma but is missing a conjunction. Avoid fragments, run-ons, and comma splices in the final versions of your written work.

See Handbook Sections 13 and 21

Practice

Circle each fragment. Draw a box around each run-on. Underline each comma splice. (1–6)

A tsunami, not a single wave but a series of waves sometimes called a wave train. Tsunamis are dangerous, they are incredibly powerful and travel very fast. Some are caused by earthquakes others are caused by volcanic eruptions. A mighty earthquake occurred under the Indian Ocean on December 26, 2004. Created a massive tsunami. Without warning, the tsunami struck Indonesia, Thailand, and other nearby countries. Caused many deaths and left millions homeless. Its powerful waves also traveled westward 3,000 miles to the coast of Africa. Death and destruction there, too.

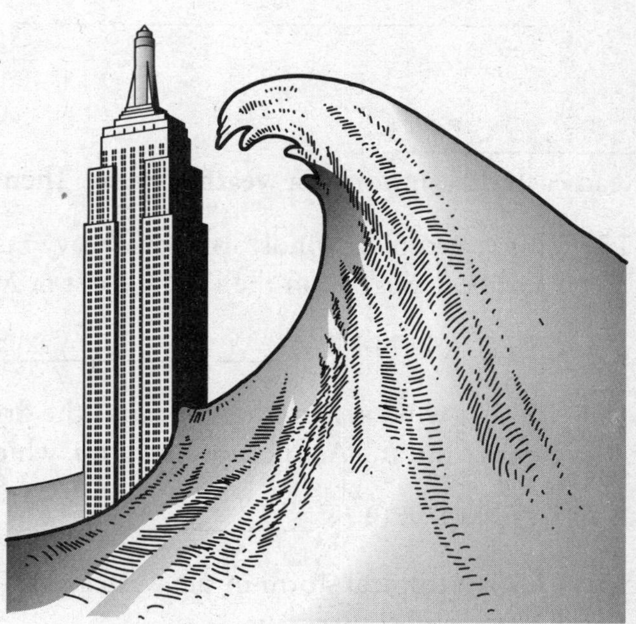

One tsunami that struck the Shetland Isles around 4950 B.C. was almost as tall as the Empire State Building.

Name ______________________

Apply

Rewrite the incorrect sentences from Practice. Correct all fragments, run-ons, and comma splices. There may be more than one way to correct the errors.

7. ______________________

____

8. ______________________

____

9. ______________________

____

10. ______________________

____

11. ______________________

____

12. ______________________

____

Reinforce

Read each description of a weather event. Then unscramble the word that names the event.

13. This is a tropical windstorm with heavy rains that starts in the Atlantic Ocean, in the Caribbean Sea, or on the Pacific coast of Mexico. It comes from the Spanish word *huracán*.

C H R A U N I R E ______________

14. This is a wind system that produces the dry and wet seasons in India and southern Asia. It comes from the Arabic word *mausim*, which means "season."

S O N O M O N ______________

15. This is a tropical storm in the western Pacific Ocean or China Sea. It comes from the Cantonese *tai fung*.

O P O N Y T H ______________

Subjects and Predicates

Underline the complete subject in each sentence. Draw a circle around the simple subject.

1. Rain is one kind of precipitation.
2. Regions with very little rain have few large animals.

Underline the complete predicate in each sentence. Draw a circle around the simple predicate.

3. Polar regions get most of their precipitation in the form of snow.
4. Winter snowpacks hold a great amount of water.

Draw one line under each compound subject in these sentences. Draw two lines under each compound predicate.

5. Texas and several neighboring states suffered terrible floods during the summer of 2007.
6. Thunderstorms flashed and boomed in June and July.
7. Creeks and rivers surged over their banks.
8. The Brazos River flooded homes and carried away cars.

Prepositions

Underline the prepositional phrase in each sentence. Draw a circle around the preposition.

9. Water surged into homes.
10. Some people climbed onto their roofs.
11. Volunteers in small boats rescued many people.

Relative Pronouns and Adverbs

Decide whether the boldfaced word in each sentence is a relative pronoun (RP) or a relative adverb (RA). Write *RP* or *RA* after each sentence to identify the boldfaced word.

12. Warning signs are posted at spots **where** visitors must be especially careful. ________
13. Hikers **who** are careful seldom have problems. ________

Direct and Indirect Objects, Predicate Nouns, and Predicate Adjectives

Write *DO* (direct object), *IO* (indirect object), *PN* (predicate noun), or *PA* (predicate adjective) to identify the boldfaced word in each sentence.

14. Usually rivers give **people** many benefits. ________
15. In 2007, however, the Brazos River became **dangerous.** ________
16. The raging river was an **enemy.** ________
17. Its surging waters flooded **neighborhoods.** ________

Dependent and Independent Clauses

Circle each sentence that has two independent clauses. Draw a box around each sentence that has one independent clause and one dependent clause.

18. Because the moist air is warm, it rises.
19. The upper air is colder, and it cannot hold all the moisture.
20. Most water vapor is invisible, but we can see water vapor in the form of clouds.

Fragments, Run-ons, and Comma Splices

Identify each item below as a comma splice, a fragment, or a run-on by writing *CS, F,* or *RO.*

21. Deserts in Australia, northern Africa, and the southwestern part of North America. ________
22. The driest desert in the world is in South America it is called the Atacama Desert. ________
23. Very little precipitation falls in Antarctica, it is considered a desert. ________

Types of Sentences

Identify each item below as a simple sentence, a compound sentence, or a complex sentence by writing *S, CD,* or *CX.*

24. Large waterfalls are spectacular sights, and Yosemite National Park incudes several of the most dramatic. ________
25. Yosemite Falls, Vernal Fall, Nevada Fall, and Bridalveil Fall are very beautiful in spring. ________
26. Hiking near the falls can be dangerous, because spray from the tumbling water makes the rocky trails slippery. ________

Spelling Practice

Read and Analyze

The Amazon flows through the South American **jungle**. It is not a **humble** stream, but a mighty river!

Write the spelling for the /əl/ sound in the words in bold type.

____

Spelling Patterns: Final Schwa with *l*

In an unstressed syllable, the vowel often has the **/ə/** sound, which is called **schwa**. The /ə/ sound is like the sound you make when you say "uh" and can be spelled with any vowel. Many words end with the /əl/ sound, which can be spelled *le* as in *battle*, *al* as in *royal*, *el* as in *vowel*, or *il* as in *pupil*.

Word Sort

Use the words below to complete the word sort.

normal	council	angle	civil
marvel	general	scramble	panel

/əl/ spelled *le*	**/əl/ spelled *al***
/əl/ spelled *el*	**/əl/ spelled *il***

Name ____________________

Pattern Practice

rural	fossil	humble
parcel	syllable	loyal

Write each word next to its meaning.

1. a word part ____________________
2. won't brag ____________________
3. trustworthy ____________________
4. in the country ____________________
5. animal in stone ____________________
6. a package ____________________

Write the word from above that completes each sentence.

7. Kara was ____________________ and told no one about her award.
8. Dad received a large ____________________ in the mail.
9. This stone has a ____________________ of an ancient insect.
10. It's nice to have a ____________________ friend I can count on.
11. Josh lives in a ____________________ area far from the city.
12. The word *home* has only one ____________________.

Use the
Dictionary

Complete each word by adding *le, al, el,* or *il.* Check your spellings in a dictionary.

13. canc__________
14. freck__________
15. festiv__________
16. utens__________

Proofreading Practice

Read this report about wetlands and find the mistakes. Use the proofreading marks below to show how each mistake should be fixed. Use a dictionary to check and correct spellings.

Proofreading Marks

Mark	Means	Example
(delete mark)	take away	Bogs and swamps are are two types of wetlands.
^	add	Bogs and swamps are two types ^of wetlands.
≡	make into an uppercase letter	bogs and swamps are two types of wetlands.
/	make into a lowercase letter	Bogs and Swamps are two types of wetlands.
⊙	add a period	Bogs and swamps are two types of wetlands⊙
(sp)	fix spelling	Boggs and swamps are two types of wetlands.

Wetlands

Wetlands are low-lying areas that are saturated with water for long periods. wetlands are classified according to the tipes of vegetation that grow in them. Swamps are wetlands that have many trees, marshes are wetlands where mostly grasses grow. Bogs are filled with different types of mosses. All three types, havens for many kinds of wildlife.

Birds throughout the world they depend on wetlands as a place to live and raise young. Many migrating birds rely on wetlands as a resting place on they're long migrations. The prairie fringed orchid and other rare plants thrive in wet, mossy bogs. Wetlands provide a natural clasroom where scientist can study a wide variety of Plant and animal life

Wetlands also teaches us about the past the chemical composition of most bogs is ideal for preserving remains. Scientists have discovered well-preserved animals and other preserved life forms in bogs all over the world. One group of scientists in florida found artifacts of a Native American people who lived 7,000 to 8,000 years ago. The items revealed that this group had advanced weaving and tool-making skills.

Although milliones of acers of wetlands in the United States been destroyed by pollution or drained for farming or industry. Many groups are working to preserve the Wetlands that remain.

Name ______________________________

Proofreading Checklist

You can use the list below to help you find and fix mistakes in your own writing. Write the titles of your own stories or reports in the blanks on top of the chart. Then use the questions to check your work. Make a check mark (✓) in each box after you have checked that item.

Proofreading Checklist for Unit 1

	Titles			
Have I joined compound sentences correctly?				
Does each sentence have both a subject and a predicate?				
Have I avoided run-on sentences, comma splices, and fragments?				
Does each sentence end with the appropriate end punctuation?				

Also Remember…

Does each sentence begin with an uppercase letter?				
Did I use a dictionary to check and correct spellings?				
Have I used commas correctly?				

Your Own List

Use this space to write your own list of things to check in your writing.

School Home Connection

In Unit 1 of *Grammar, Usage, and Mechanics,* we are learning about different types of sentences and about the important parts of a sentence. The activities on this page give extra practice with some of the concepts we're learning. You can help your child use the information he or she is learning in school by choosing one or more activities to complete with your child at home.

Sentence Scramble **(Complete Subjects and Complete Predicates)**

With your child, read the weather forecasts in your local newspaper. Ask your child to copy four sentences from the forecasts onto strips of paper. Have your child underline the complete subject and circle the complete predicate. (The subject is the part of the sentence that tells whom or what the sentence is about. The predicate is the part of the sentence that tells what happens.)

Example Wednesday will be sunny.

Rain is expected by Friday.

Then snip the strips in half between the subject and predicate, and scramble the parts to make silly new sentences.

Example Rain will be sunny.

Wednesday is expected by Friday.

Back Then **(Simple Subjects and Simple Predicates)**

Have your child interview an older relative or friend and ask that person what life was like when he or she was in the fifth grade. Have your child record the conversation or take notes. Afterward, help your child write three sentences about the interview. Ask your child to underline the simple subject and circle the simple predicate in each sentence. (The simple subject is the most important word or phrase in the subject. The simple predicate is the verb that tells what the subject did, or links the subject to descriptive information.)

Example Grandma rode a trolley car to school.

She worked in her parents' restaurant after school.

Her friend had a pet donkey.

Name ____

Able to Leap Tall Buildings **(Simple and Compound Sentences)**

Ask your child to think of some superhuman power he or she would like to have. Then have your child write three compound sentences about how things are now and how they would be different if he or she had that power. (A compound sentence is two separate sentences joined by a comma and *and, or,* or *but.*)

Example If your child chooses the power to fly, he or she might write, "Now it takes me forty minutes to get to school by bus, but with the power to fly, I could get there in five minutes!"

Work with your child to underline the conjunction *and, or,* or *but* in each sentence.

Find the Shoe **(Prepositional Phrases)**

You can play this game with the whole family. First, have the other players close their eyes. Then take a shoe and hide it somewhere in the room. Have the other players guess where the shoe is, using prepositional phrases. (A prepositional phrase can tell where something is. Prepositional phrases begin with words such as *in, under, through,* or *beyond.*)

Example Is it in the refrigerator? Is it under the sink?

When a player asks a question, have him or her identify the prepositional phrase in the question and then go look for the shoe. When the shoe has been found, the finder can then hide the shoe.

What Is Wrong? **(Prepositional Phrases)**

Ask your child to write three sentences about what is wrong with this picture. Then work with your child to identify any prepositional phrases he or she used. (Prepositional phrases begin with words such as *around, at, by, for, from, in, near, of, off, on, to,* or *with.*)

Example The cow is floating in the air.

Thanks to the bravery of **Samuel Wilson**, the town of **Metonymy** was saved from the British. When the **Revolutionary War** began, Sam was eight years old. He was given the job of drummer boy in his **town**. When he saw the **redcoats** coming, Sam banged his **drum**. He alerted the **townspeople** in time for them to stop the **soldiers**.

Circle the boldfaced words that name particular persons, places, things, or ideas.

A **common noun** names any person, place, thing, or idea. A **proper noun** names a particular person, place, thing, or idea. Proper nouns must be capitalized.

See Handbook Section 14

Practice

Underline each common noun. Circle each proper noun.

1. Sam Wilson later started a plant for packing meat in Troy, New York.
2. Because of his friendliness, Sam was called "Uncle Sam" by his workers.
3. During the War of 1812, Sam printed *U.S.* on the meat being sent to the army.
4. A curious inspector asked a worker what the letters stood for.
5. The worker didn't know, so he said they might stand for *Uncle Sam.*
6. Soon people all over America were saying that things that came from the government were from Uncle Sam.
7. Uncle Sam has been a national symbol ever since.
8. Illustrators started printing pictures of Uncle Sam in newspapers in 1820.
9. The most famous picture of Uncle Sam was painted by James Montgomery Flagg.
10. This painting was used on recruiting posters for the U.S. Army during World War I.
11. In striped pants and top hat, Uncle Sam is still seen in ads and political cartoons.

James Flagg's painting of Uncle Sam is still widely used today.

Name ______________________________

Apply

Uncle Sam is a symbol used to represent the United States of America. Write four sentences about other symbols of our nation. Use nouns from the word bank or think of your own. Be sure to capitalize proper nouns.

bald eagle	Old Glory	the Liberty Bell
flag	Stars and Stripes	the White House

12. ______________________________

____

13. ______________________________

____

14. ______________________________

____

15. ______________________________

____

Reinforce

Circle the eight hidden nouns.
Write the proper nouns below.
Use proper capitalization.

Proper Nouns

16. ______________

17. ______________

18. ______________

19. ______________

I	J	S	B	F	R	O	P	Q	R
N	E	X	P	L	Q	G	U	G	W
D	F	S	A	S	X	P	K	Y	A
E	F	I	R	E	W	O	R	K	S
P	E	H	A	P	L	Q	U	X	H
E	R	Z	D	H	M	R	V	Y	I
N	S	C	E	I	K	S	W	Z	N
D	O	V	Q	J	O	F	L	A	G
E	N	B	R	K	P	T	M	P	T
N	L	I	N	C	O	L	N	R	O
C	Z	H	Z	D	V	N	A	Z	N
E	A	A	M	E	R	I	C	A	M

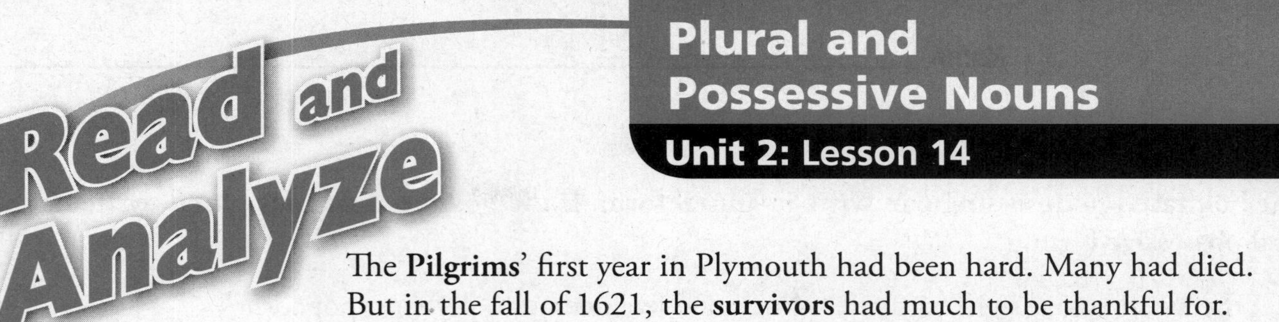

Plural and Possessive Nouns

The **Pilgrims'** first year in Plymouth had been hard. Many had died. But in the fall of 1621, the **survivors** had much to be thankful for.

Circle the part of the word *Pilgrims'* that shows possession.

Circle the part of the word *survivors* that shows it is talking about more than one person.

A **plural noun** names more than one person, place, thing, or idea. Most nouns add *-s* or *-es* to form the plural. Some nouns change spelling instead of adding *-s* or *-es* (*woman, women*). Some nouns have the same singular and plural form (*deer*). Plurals formed in ways other than adding *-s* or *-es* are called **irregular plural nouns**. A **possessive noun** shows ownership. Most plural nouns add an apostrophe after the *-s* to form the possessive (*boys'*). Plurals that don't end in *-s*, such as *men,* add apostrophe and *-s* to show possession (*men's*).

See Handbook Sections 25 and 26

Practice

Draw a box around each noun that is both plural and possessive. For the remaining nouns, underline each plural noun and circle each possessive noun.

1. The colonists' Patuxet friend Squanto had helped them build houses and plant crops.
2. The colony's governor had made peace with Massasoit, chief of the Wampanoag.
3. The settlers' harvest was expected to be good.
4. The colonists planned to invite the Wampanoag to a celebration.
5. Four women and two teenagers cooked food for 147 people.
6. The group's celebration lasted three days.
7. Unfortunately, the next year's harvest was not as good.
8. The settlers did not hold another celebration.
9. Americans did not celebrate Thanksgiving again until 1777.
10. Sarah Josepha Hale tried for more than 30 years to make Thanksgiving a holiday.
11. President Lincoln's proclamation in 1863 made Hale's wish come true.
12. Americans celebrate Thanksgiving on the fourth Thursday of November.

Women ground corn to make bread and biscuits for the first Thanksgiving.

Lesson 14 Name ______________________

Apply

If the boldfaced noun is singular, write its plural form. If the boldfaced noun is plural, write its plural possessive form.

13. The Wampanoag's **gift** to the feast included five **deer** and, perhaps, popcorn.

    ______________________ ______________________

14. The **celebration** probably began with a blare of **bugles** and a parade.

    ______________________ ______________________

15. Everyone feasted on wild **birds, pumpkins,** and cranberries.

    ______________________ ______________________

16. For entertainment, the **men** competed in foot races and jumping **matches.**

    ______________________ ______________________

17. The **friendship** lasted until 1675, when **war** broke out over land disputes.

    ______________________ ______________________

18. Today, **visitors** to Plymouth can tour a village just like the one the **Pilgrims** built.

    ______________________ ______________________

Reinforce

See Handbook Section 32

Ask an adult to help you search the Internet to learn more about the first Thanksgiving. Write a paragraph telling what you learned. Use at least one plural noun and one possessive noun.

____

____

____

____

____

____

____

____

Read and Analyze

Concrete, Abstract, and Collective Nouns

Unit 2: Lesson 15

Each **group** that set out for the West in **wagons** in the 1840s faced **danger** along the trail.

Circle the boldfaced word that names a collection of people. Draw one line under the boldfaced word that names items that could be seen, touched, smelled, heard, or tasted. Draw two lines under the boldfaced word that names an idea.

A **collective noun** names a group of people or things. A **concrete noun** names something you can see, touch, hear, smell, or taste. An **abstract noun** names an idea.

See Handbook Section 14

Practice

Read each sentence. Circle the boldfaced word that is the type of noun listed in parentheses.

1. One **party** that met disaster on the **trail** west was the Donner Party. (collective noun)
2. In May of 1846, 81 **people** left Independence, Missouri, filled with **hope**. (concrete noun)
3. They decided to follow a route recommended in a **letter** from Lansford W. Hastings, whose **knowledge** of the trail was faulty. (abstract noun)
4. The route would take the Donner party off the main trail, through rugged **mountains**, and across the **emptiness** of the Great Salt Lake Desert. (concrete noun)
5. When this **band** of pioneers left the main trail to follow Hastings' cutoff, Tamsen Donner felt **sadness**, for she did not trust Hastings. (collective noun)
6. The trail through the Wasatch Mountains was too steep, rough, and narrow for the party's **wagons**, so on many days they made little **progress**. (abstract noun)
7. The weary **bunch** of pioneers did not make it out of the mountains until early September, and food and **supplies** were running short. (collective noun)
8. They crossed the desert in searing heat, with very little **water** to quench their **thirst**. (concrete noun)
9. By the time the Donner Party reached the high Sierra Nevada, **snow** blocked the trail and left them stranded for the **winter** with very little food. (abstract noun)
10. Only 45 of the 81 members of the **group** survived the terrible **ordeal**. (collective noun)

Name ______________________________

Apply

Write complete sentences to answer these questions. Circle each collective noun you write. Draw a line under each abstract noun you write.

11. In addition to bravery, what character trait do you think pioneers needed most?

____

____

12. Is fearlessness or cautiousness a better trait for a pioneer to possess? Tell why you think so.

____

____

13. What types of people would you choose as members of a party of pioneers?

____

____

14. What feelings do you think you would experience as a pioneer on a difficult journey?

____

____

Reinforce

Many types of animals have special collective nouns to name groups of them. For example, a group of crows can be called a *murder* of crows. Draw lines to connect each collective noun below to the animal it is used with. Then, on the lines below, write a sentence using one of these collective nouns.

hogs	peep
larks	parliament
chickens	exaltation
foxes	skulk
owls	drift

____

____

____

Read and Analyze

Personal and Possessive Pronouns

Unit 2: Lesson 16

In the early 1890s Katharine Lee Bates, a professor from Massachusetts, visited Colorado. While there, **she** climbed Pikes Peak. The view from the summit was so magnificent that Miss Bates was inspired to write a poem. **Its** first line was "O beautiful for spacious skies."

To whom does the word *she* refer? ______________________________

What word does *Its* stand for? ______________________________

A **pronoun** can take the place of a noun. Use the **personal pronouns** *I, me, we,* and *us* to speak or write about yourself. Use *she, her, it, he, him, you, they,* and *them* to refer to other people and things. The **possessive pronouns** *his, its, our, her, their, my,* and *your* show ownership. **Remember to use this information when you speak, too.**

See Handbook Section 16

Practice

Circle each personal pronoun in the sentences below. Underline each possessive pronoun.

1. Her poem was matched with the melody of a hymn called "Materna."
2. It had been written by Samuel A. Ward thirteen years earlier.
3. His melody fit perfectly with the verses she had written.
4. The result of their creative talents was the song "America the Beautiful."
5. Some of us find that song easier to sing than "The Star-Spangled Banner."
6. We would prefer to have "America the Beautiful" become our national anthem.
7. I am not a good singer, but "The Star-Spangled Banner" is one of my favorite songs.
8. It was written by Francis Scott Key during the War of 1812 and quickly became the unofficial national anthem.
9. The sight of the American flag flying after a fierce battle was his inspiration for writing "The Star-Spangled Banner."
10. More than 100 years later, President Herbert Hoover made its status as national anthem official.

Bates's poem became "America the Beautiful."

Name ______________________________

Apply

Rewrite each sentence, replacing each underlined word with a pronoun from the box. More than one pronoun may be correct. Remember to capitalize a pronoun that begins a sentence.

they	them	we	us	it	its	she	her	their

11. Katharine Lee Bates would be pleased to know that Katharine Lee Bates's poem remains popular more than a century after the poem was written. ______________________________

____

12. Many of the residents of the United States know the song's first verse by heart. ______________________________

____

13. School children across America sing this song often. ______________________________

____

14. Patriotic songs can help people express people's pride in people's country. ______________________________

____

15. America's national anthem is played at most sports events. ______________________________

____

Reinforce

Do you think that "America the Beautiful" should become our national anthem? Write two or three sentences to explain how you feel and why. Circle personal and possessive pronouns.

____

____

____

____

____

____

____

Action Verbs and Linking Verbs

The Mississippi **is** America's biggest river. Its name **means** "big river." The Illinois, Kickapoo, Ojibway, and Santee Dakota peoples **are** long-time residents of the upper Mississippi Valley. They **gave** the river its name.

Underline the two boldfaced words that tell about actions. Circle the two boldfaced words that link subjects with words that tell about them.

An **action verb** tells what the subject of a sentence does. (*She shares her books.*) A **linking verb** links the subject with words that tell what the subject is or is like. (*She is friendly.*) Linking verbs include *am, is, are, was, were, become,* and *seem.*

See Handbook Section 17

Practice

Underline each boldfaced word that is an action verb. Circle each boldfaced word that is a linking verb. (1–10)

The first Europeans **traveled** on the Mississippi River in 1541. The river **became** vital to agriculture and industry about 200 years ago.

Today barges constantly **move** important goods up and down the Mississippi. Tugboats **guide** the barges past hazardous areas. Cargoes on southbound barges **are** usually agricultural products. Northbound barges **haul** machinery and fuel.

The lands beside the southern Mississippi River **are** fertile. Spring floods **added** important nutrients to the land for centuries.

New Orleans **is** the southernmost large city on the Mississippi. Workers there **load** cargoes of all kinds onto ships bound for ports all over the world.

Name ______________________________

Apply

Complete each sentence with a verb from the word bank. Write *A* if it is an action verb and *L* if it is a linking verb.

contain	flows	is	marks	becomes

11. The Nile River ________________ the longest river in the world. ______
12. The Colorado river ________________ through the southwestern United States and northwest Mexico. ______
13. Most rivers ________________ fresh water. ______
14. The Amazon River ________________ several times wider during the wet season. ______
15. The Rhine ________________ the border between Germany and France. ______

Reinforce

Suppose you are a captain of a tugboat that hauls barges on the Mississippi River. Write a paragraph about what you typically see and do on a downriver run. Use at least two action verbs and two linking verbs in your descriptive paragraph.

____

____

____

____

____

____

____

____

____

____

____

____

Read and Analyze

Up until late 1953, doctors **could** not **give** leukemia patients any hope for survival. This lesson **will acquaint** you with a researcher responsible for the first effective leukemia treatments.

Circle the more important boldfaced verb in each sentence. Underline the other boldfaced verb.

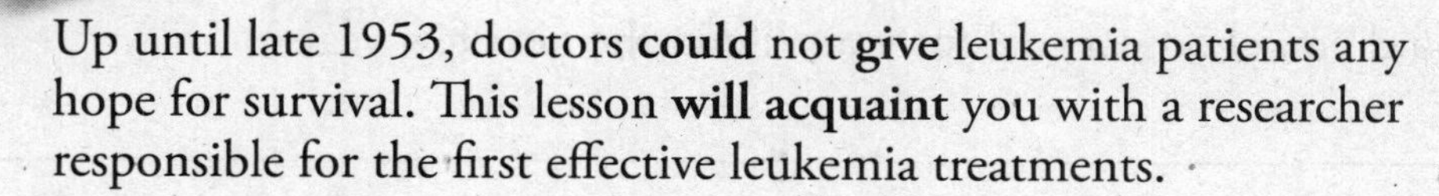

The **main verb** is the most important verb in a sentence. A **helping verb** may come before the main verb.

See Handbook Section 17

Practice

In each sentence, circle the main verb and underline the helping verb.

1. Gertrude B. Elion was born in 1918 in New York City.
2. Before her first day of college, Gertrude had chosen a goal.
3. She would find a cure for cancer.
4. She did pursue that goal through the study of chemistry in college.
5. Despite her academic success in college, research labs would not hire Elion as a researcher.
6. Lab directors would give only males jobs as chemists.
7. During World War II, labs could not find enough male chemists.
8. Elion was hired by a pharmaceutical company.
9. Many differences between disease-causing cells and normal cells were identified by Elion and her research partner, George Hitchings.
10. With this knowledge, Elion and Hitchings could create the first drug effective against leukemia.
11. Drugs effective against HIV and gout were also developed by Elion and Hitchings.
12. In 1988 the two were awarded the Nobel Prize in Physiology and Medicine.

Gertrude B. Elion was a Nobel Prize winner.

Name ______________________________

Apply

Write a sentence to answer each question. Underline each helping verb you use.

13. Could you choose a goal for your life in the next few years?

____

____

14. What might your goal be?

____

____

15. What subjects would you study for your work toward this goal?

____

____

16. How else could you prepare yourself for the pursuit of this goal?

____

____

Reinforce

The word search puzzle below contains all 23 commonly used helping verbs. Circle each one. Then write them on the lines.

B	E	I	N	G	Q	S	H	O	U	L	D
E	X	S	R	H	A	D	A	X	C	Z	L
E	D	I	D	S	R	O	V	H	A	S	C
N	O	Q	V	W	E	R	E	T	N	M	O
X	E	B	E	I	M	A	Y	J	B	U	U
A	S	H	A	L	L	X	B	W	A	S	L
M	W	O	U	L	D	M	I	G	H	T	D

Across: ____

Down: ____

Read and Analyze

Modal Auxiliaries

"You **should** join our group," Sidney said to Carlos. "With your help, we **can** create the best history project in the school!"

Circle the boldfaced helping verb which indicates the ability to do something. Underline the boldfaced helping verb which expresses a duty or an obligation.

The helping verbs *may* and *might* can be used to ask or give permission. The helping verbs *can* and *could* can be used to indicate ability. The helping verbs *should* and *must* can be used to communicate a duty or an obligation. The helping verbs *may, might, could, should,* and *will* can be used to indicate possibility—how likely something is to happen. Helping verbs that have these special functions are called **modal auxiliaries**.

See Handbook Section 17

Practice

Circle the modal auxiliary in each sentence. Then underline the word in parentheses that tells about its special function.

1. We will create an illustrated timeline of the American Civil War. (possibility/ability)
2. May I be in charge of photo research for the project? (obligation/permission)
3. We should follow the rules for safe use of the Internet. (obligation/ability)
4. That website might show a diagram of the Battle of Gettysburg. (possibility/ability)
5. You must reduce photographs to the proper size for the timeline. (permission/obligation)
6. This photograph of General Robert E. Lee on his horse, Traveller, will illustrate the entry "Seven Days Before Richmond" in 1862. (possibility/ability)
7. You should easily find a photograph of the Sharpsburg Bridge at Antietam. (permission/possibility)
8. The media director says that we may use the color printer for reproductions of paintings. (obligation/permission)
9. The writers might finish the event cards tomorrow. (possibility/ability)

Robert E. Lee served as the military leader of the Confederacy during the Civil War.

Name ______________________________

Apply

Use one of the modal auxiliaries in the word bank to complete each sentence.

should	could	will	can	may	must

10. Most Americans ______________ name the President who was in office during the Civil War.
11. A serious student of the Civil War ______________ read the Gettysburg Address.
12. With some effort you ________________ memorize this brief speech.
13. Any history textbook with information about the Civil War ________________ mention the Battle of Gettysburg.
14. You ______________ know that President Abraham Lincoln remembered soldiers' heroism in the Battle of Gettysburg when he dedicated a cemetery there on November 19, 1863.

Reinforce

Write five sentences telling a student what she or he can do to learn more about the American Civil War. Use a modal auxiliary in each sentence.

____

____

____

____

____

____

____

____

____

____

____

____

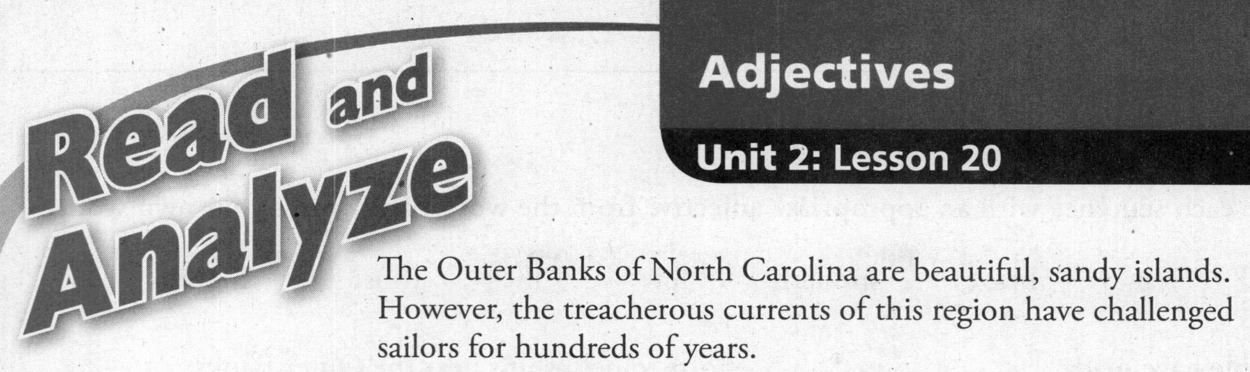

Adjectives

Unit 2: Lesson 20

The Outer Banks of North Carolina are beautiful, sandy islands. However, the treacherous currents of this region have challenged sailors for hundreds of years.

Circle the two words that tell what the islands are like. Circle one word that tells what the currents are like.

Adjectives describe nouns and pronouns. Some adjectives tell what kind. Others, like *many* and *six,* tell how many. The adjectives *this, that, these,* and *those* tell which one. These are called *demonstrative adjectives*. The articles *a, an,* and *the* are also adjectives.

See Handbook Section 15

Practice

Some adjectives in these sentences appear in boldfaced type. Circle each boldfaced adjective that tells what kind. Underline each boldfaced adjective that tells how many. Draw a box around each boldfaced adjective that tells which one. Underline each boldfaced article (*a, an, the*) twice.

1. One of **the** United States' most **famous** historical sights was built to warn sailors of the **dangerous** waters of the Outer Banks.
2. **Two** currents collide near Cape Hatteras, causing **powerful** waves.
3. A **treacherous** reef called Diamond Shoals also lies in **the** area.
4. **This** combination has caused many shipwrecks over **the** centuries.
5. Hurricanes sometimes strike **this** area as well.
6. For **all these** reasons, it is known as **the** Graveyard of **the** Atlantic.
7. In 1870, **a striped** lighthouse was built on Cape Hatteras to warn ships.
8. At **208** feet, it is **the tallest** lighthouse in **the** United States.
9. **This historic** lighthouse still stands today, and it is visited by **many** tourists **each** year.
10. **the** Outer Banks are **beautiful** and **interesting** as well as **dangerous**.
11. Tourists come to **the** Cape Hatteras National Seashore to visit **the gorgeous** beaches.
12. Nearby is Kitty Hawk, where **the** Wright brothers made their **famous** flight.

The Cape Hatteras Lighthouse is endangered by beach erosion.

Name ______________________________

Apply

Complete each sentence with an appropriate adjective from the word bank or use your own word.

that	ten	brave	modern	few	the	those	heroic

13. People have made ________________ efforts to help ships near the Outer Banks.
14. In 1899, Rasmus S. Midgett saved ________________ men from a sinking ship during a hurricane.
15. ________________ men would have died without him.
16. Mr. Midgett was a ________________ member of the U.S. Life-Saving Service.
17. ________________ service joined the Coast Guard in 1915.
18. Today the Coast Guard uses ________________ technology to find and help ships in trouble near Cape Hatteras.
19. As a result, ________________ ships have been wrecked in recent years.

Reinforce

Use these clues to complete the puzzle.

Across

5. A _____ adjective tells which one is being talked about.
6. The word _____ is an article.
7. *This, that, these,* and _____ are demonstrative adjectives.

Down

1. An adjective may _____ a noun.
2. Adjectives such as *two* and *few* tell _____ many.
3. *A* is a special kind of adjective called an _____.
4. Most adjectives come _____ the nouns they tell about.

Read and Analyze

The whaling industry was **very** important to the United States in the early 1800s. During that time, whalers **expertly** hunted thousands of whales each year.

Which boldfaced word tells how people do something? ______________

Which boldfaced word describes an adjective and tells how much?

____

Adverbs describe verbs or adjectives. They tell how, when, where, or to what extent (how much). Many adverbs end in *-ly*. Other common adverbs are *fast, very, often, again, sometimes, soon, only, however, too, later, first, then, far,* and *now*.

See Handbook Section 18

Practice

Circle each adverb below.

1. American whalers first hunted sperm whales in the 1700s.
2. The oils from sperm whales were extremely valuable then.
3. These oils were used chiefly for lamps.
4. Whaling voyages sometimes lasted for four or five years.
5. When the California gold rush started suddenly in 1849, many whalers quickly abandoned their ships to seek their fortunes on land.

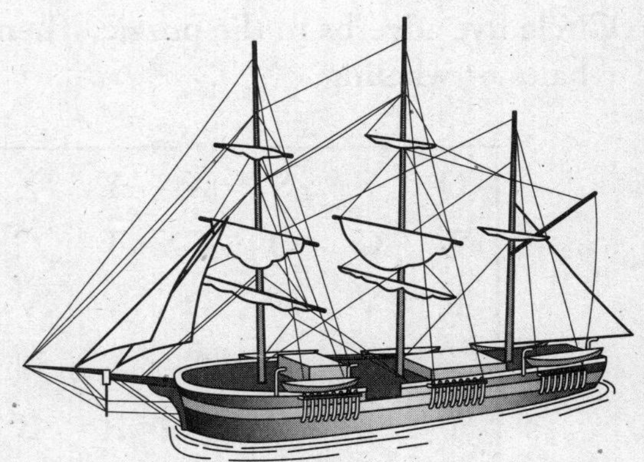

Whalers like this one sailed the high seas in search of whales.

6. The American whaling industry declined rapidly after the Civil War.
7. Soon only a few whaling operations remained in the United States.
8. However, the whaling industries of other nations expanded dramatically in the late 1800s.
9. New technology helped whalers catch and process whales efficiently.
10. Tragically, the whalers killed many thousands of whales.
11. Many species were nearly made extinct.
12. Now commercial whaling is illegal in the United States and most other countries.
13. The population of many whale species has risen significantly.

Lesson 21

Name ______________________________

Apply

Circle the adverb that tells more about each underlined word or words. Then tell whether the adverb explains *how, when, where,* or *to what extent.*

14. Humpback whales <u>migrate</u> yearly between polar and tropical regions. ______________

15. Because humpbacks <u>swim</u> slowly, they used to be easy prey for whalers. ______________

16. The commercial whaling of humpbacks finally <u>ended</u> in the 1960s. ______________

17. Many humpbacks accidentally <u>become</u> entangled in fishing nets. ______________

18. If a whale <u>is caught</u> there it usually drowns or starves to death. ______________

19. Whales that <u>struggle</u> frantically may tear an expensive net to shreds. ______________

20. Experts cut a net so that the whale <u>can swim</u> free and the net can be fixed. ______________

Reinforce

Circle five adverbs in the puzzle. Then choose two of the adverbs. Use each in a sentence about whales or whaling.

Q	F	S	X	Y	X	W	Q	J
W	G	O	C	T	C	R	T	K
R	V	M	D	V	V	T	S	L
T	R	E	C	E	N	T	L	Y
Y	J	T	B	R	B	Y	O	N
P	X	I	N	Y	N	D	W	V
S	L	M	Q	R	M	G	L	Y
T	H	E	R	E	S	K	Y	W
D	Z	S	Q	W	D	Z	K	Z

21. ____

____

22. ____

____

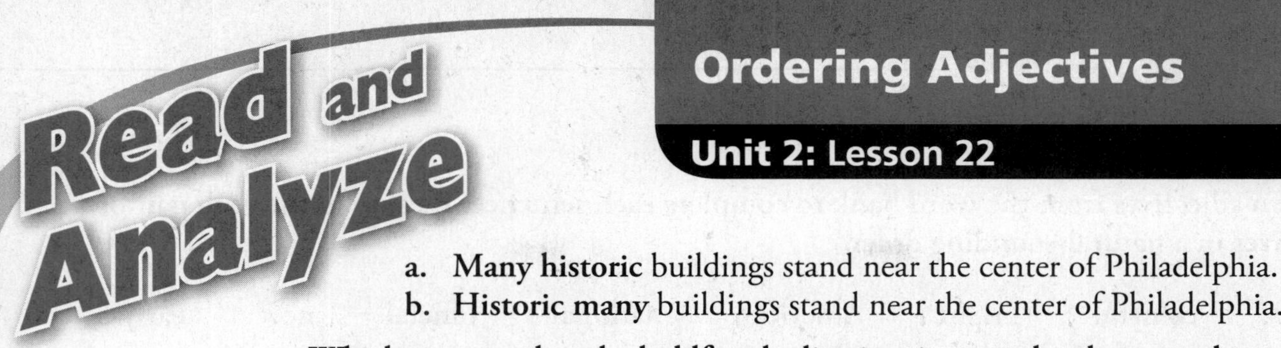

Ordering Adjectives

Unit 2: Lesson 22

a. **Many historic** buildings stand near the center of Philadelphia.
b. **Historic many** buildings stand near the center of Philadelphia.

Which sentence has the boldfaced adjectives in an order that sounds natural? ____

When you use more than one adjective to describe a noun, put the adjectives in an order that sounds natural. This chart can help you put pairs of adjectives in a natural-sounding order:

See Handbook Section 15

how many	what quality	how big	how old	what shape	what color	what material	→ noun
three	*beautiful*	*small*	*new*	*round*	*pink*	*silken*	→ *petals*

Practice

Underline the adjectives in parentheses that are in an order that sounds natural.

1. Philadelphia is (an eastern large/a large eastern) city.
2. It was a (busy young/young busy) city in the mid-1700s.
3. Around 1764, (some successful/successful some) Philadelphians became opposed to English rule.
4. They met with leaders of (other American/American other) colonies to consider independence.
5. In 1776 (colonial brave/brave colonial) leaders signed a document declaring America's independence from England.
6. In 1789 a group of the new nation's leaders wrote a (remarkable new/new remarkable) document that established our country's legal system.

Both the Declaration of Independence and the United States Constitution were signed in Independence Hall in Philadelphia.

7. These (two famous/famous two) documents, the Declaration of Independence and the United States Constitution, were both signed in Independence Hall in Philadelphia.

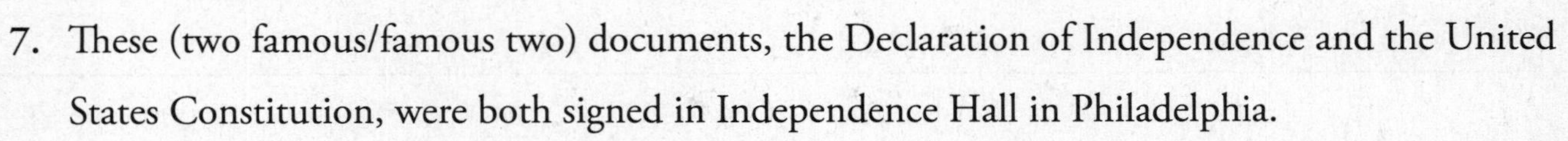

8. Built of (red strong/strong red) bricks, this building still stands in the heart of Philadelphia.
9. This (handsome old/old handsome) building is in Independence National Historic Park.
10. You can also see the (silver large/large silver) bell known as the Liberty Bell, which was sounded when colonial representatives approved the Declaration of Independence.

Name ______________________________

Apply

Use two adjectives from the word bank to complete each sentence. Be sure to use each pair of adjectives in a natural-sounding order.

red	colorful	bright	American	national	official	new	early

11. Betsy Ross's family members claimed that she sewed a ______________________ flag in 1776.
12. According to them, Betsy Ross created this ______________________ flag in a house on Arch Street in Philadelphia.
13. On the first version of our American flag, ______________________ stripes alternated with white stripes, and thirteen white stars formed a circle on a field of blue.
14. The stars-and-stripes design was approved by Congress on June 14, 1777, and that day is now an ______________________ holiday.

Reinforce

Write a descriptive paragraph about a symbol of America, such as the American flag, the Statue of Liberty, the White House, or the bald eagle. Use a pair of adjectives with one of the nouns you include.

____

____

____

____

____

____

____

____

____

Coordinating and Subordinating Conjunctions

Unit 2: Lesson 23

a. Mount Rushmore features enormous carvings of George Washington, Thomas Jefferson, Theodore Roosevelt, and Abraham Lincoln.

b. I recommend seeing it because it is so unusual.

Which word in sentence *a* links several proper nouns? __________

Which word in sentence *b* links the first part of the sentence to the second part of the sentence? ________________

Coordinating conjunctions (*and, but, or*) connect words or groups of words (including independent clauses) that are similar. **Subordinating conjunctions,** such as *although, because, if,* and *before,* show how one clause is related to another clause. Subordinating conjunctions appear at the beginning of dependent clauses.

See Handbook Section 21

Practice

Underline each coordinating conjunction and circle each subordinating conjunction.

1. Doane Robinson had the idea to carve sculptures into Mount Rushmore, but he didn't think of portraying American presidents.
2. His idea was to carve legendary Westerners Kit Carson, Jim Bridger, and John Colter.
3. Gutzon Borglum wanted to make carvings of presidents because presidents are important.

The faces of four American presidents stare across the prairies of South Dakota.

4. Borglum was hired because he had already carved statues in the sides of mountains.
5. If Borglum had not had experience, the project probably would have failed.
6. The peak could be reached only by foot or horseback.
7. Equipment had to be hauled up thousands of feet and then lowered by ropes to work areas.
8. Dynamite and steam drills were used to blast away rock.
9. Although Borglum died before the project was finished, his son Lincoln did complete it.
10. It took 14 years and nearly one million dollars to complete the sculpture.

Name ____

Apply

Complete each sentence with a conjunction from the word bank. Write *C* if it is a coordinating conjunction and *S* if it is a subordinating conjunction.

although	and	or	because	but	before

11. ________________ Americans do not often create giant monuments anymore, many still admire those created in the past. _____

12. Borglum started out as a painter, __________ he became a sculptor in later life. _____

13. Visitors to Mount Rushmore are often surprised ______________ the carved heads are much paler than the uncarved rock around them. _____

14. The heads are sixty feet high, __________ the mouths are eighteen feet wide. _____

15. Almost every visitor to Mount Rushmore takes photographs ________ buys postcards of the huge monument. _____

16. ________________ I saw Mount Rushmore, I had no idea of its huge size. _____

Reinforce

Write the name of each president on Mount Rushmore next to the statement that describes him. Then circle the conjunction in each sentence.

17. Before he became America's first president, he was a surveyor.

    ____

18. People may admire him for crafting The Declaration of Independence and for bringing the recipe for ice cream to America. ____

19. Since he once spared a bear cub during a hunting trip, a toy bear was named for him.

    ____

20. His Gettysburg Address contains only ten sentences, yet it is considered one of the greatest speeches of all time. ____

Read and Analyze

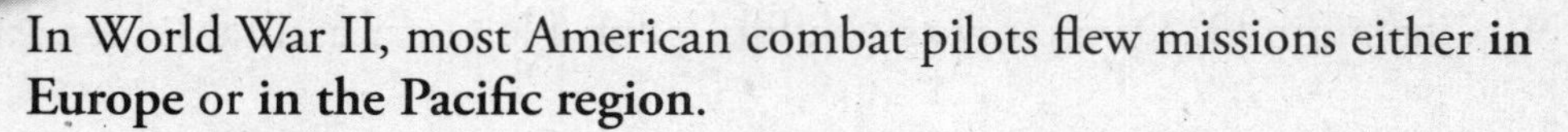
In World War II, most American combat pilots flew missions either **in Europe** or **in the Pacific region.**

Circle the two words that link the boldfaced phrases.

Correlative conjunctions always appear in pairs. They connect words or groups of words and provide more emphasis than coordinating conjunctions. Some common correlative conjunctions are *both . . . and, either . . . or, neither . . . nor, not only . . . but (also),* and *whether . . . or.*

See Handbook Section 21

Practice

Circle the correlative conjunctions and coordinating conjunctions in these sentences. If a sentence contains correlative conjunctions, write *COR.* If the sentence does not contain correlative conjunctions, write *X.*

1. Neither the U.S. Army nor the U.S. Navy would allow African Americans to fly planes before 1941. __________
2. In the 1930s African American leaders argued for training for African American military pilots, and a program was established in 1940. __________
3. Successful candidates were brought to Tuskegee Army Air Field in Alabama, and there they were commanded by Captain Benjamin O. Davis. __________
4. The first group from Tuskegee, which included both airmen and support personnel, headed for combat in Italy in April of 1943. __________
5. The Tuskegee Airmen performed well in Sicily, and their unit received a Distinguished Unit Citation. __________
6. Most of these pilots' missions during the rest of the war involved flying along with bombers and protecting them from German planes. __________
7. The Tuskegee Airmen proved to be both courageous and skillful as they helped the Allies defeat Adolf Hitler. __________
8. Whether they received medals for individual acts of bravery or just helped with their squadrons' missions, all Tuskegee Airmen earned the right to be called American heroes.

   ____

Name ______________________________

Apply

Rewrite each sentence pair as one sentence using the correlative conjunctions in parentheses.

9. Benjamin O. Davis Jr. was a skillful pilot. He was a natural leader. (not only/but also)

____

____

10. He fought in World War II. He fought in the Korean War. (both/and)

____

____

11. Benjamin O. Davis Jr. always performed excellently in service to America. He was serving as a general in the Air Force. He was leading a government agency. (whether/or)

____

____

Reinforce

Write a paragraph about someone you know or have read about who has performed an important service for our nation. Use at least one pair of correlative conjunctions in your paragraph.

____

____

____

____

____

____

____

____

____

____

Nouns

Write whether the boldfaced word is a proper noun or a common noun. Then circle each boldfaced noun that is plural. Underline each one that is possessive.

1. **America's** first hard-surfaced road was the Lancaster Turnpike in Pennsylvania.

   ____

2. Until the automobile became popular, few **roads** in America were paved. ____________________

Read each sentence. Circle the boldfaced word that is the type of noun listed in parentheses.

3. A **crew** on a steam railroad **train** consisted of a conductor, an engineer, a fireman, and a brakeman. (collective noun)
4. When a new railroad line reached a frontier **town**, residents could share news and **gossip** more quickly with relatives in the East. (abstract noun)
5. Trains carried **sacks** of mail back and forth between **civilization** and the frontier. (concrete noun)

Pronouns

Rewrite each sentence. Use a pronoun in place of each boldfaced word or phrase.

6. In 1820, **Major Stephen Long** said that Nebraska was nearly a desert and that **Nebraska** could not support crops. ____________________

   ____

7. **Major Long's** opinion about **Nebraska's** suitability for growing crops was wrong.

   ____

8. In Nebraska today, **farmers and ranchers** produce huge amounts of grain and meat for **you and me** to eat. ____________________

   ____

Verbs

Write *action verb* or *linking verb* to identify the type of each boldfaced verb.

9. The United States **doubled** in size in 1803. ____________________

10. Thomas Jefferson **was** President of the United States then. ____________________

Circle the main verb in each sentence. Underline the helping verb.

11. The first official coins of the United States of America were issued in 1792.

12. The museums of the Smithsonian do not charge admission.

13. You can see hundreds of rare and valuable coins on a visit to the Smithsonian.

Circle the modal auxiliary in each sentence. Then underline the word in parentheses that tells about its specific function.

14. May I borrow that book about Seattle? (possibility/permission)

15. This chapter might discuss the construction of the Space Needle. (possibility/obligation)

Adjectives and Adverbs

Circle the boldfaced words that are adjectives. Underline the boldfaced words that are adverbs.

16. Boats floated **swiftly** down the Mississippi River with goods from the **fertile** Ohio Valley.

17. The river currents flowed too **violently** for the boatmen to row upriver **safely**.

18. They **wearily** rode the **long** way home on horseback along the Natchez Trace.

Read each sentence and the adjectives in parentheses. Write those adjectives in the blank in the order that sounds natural.

19. The state of Hawaii includes ____________________ islands. (main, five)

20. The island of Kauai is known for its ____________________ valleys. (lush, green)

Conjunctions

Draw one line under each coordinating conjunction. Draw two lines under each subordinating conjunction. Circle each correlative conjunction.

21. When immigrants arrived in America in the late 1800s, they went through an approval process.

22. Some immigrants were ill, and they were sent back home.

23. Intake centers were maintained on both the East Coast and the West Coast.

Spelling Practice

Do you remember how many U.S. presidents first served as governor of their state?

Write the two words in the sentence that end with the /ər/ sound.

____

Spelling Patterns: Final Schwa + *n,* Final Schwa + *r*

In an unstressed syllable, the vowel often has the /ə/ sound. The /ə/ sound is like the sound you make when you say "uh" and can be spelled with any vowel. Many words end with the /ər/ sound, which can be spelled *er* as in *water* or *or* as in *tractor*. The ending /ən/ sound can be spelled *en* as in *lighten*, *on* as in *onion*, or *ion* as in *million*.

Word Sort

Use the words below to complete the word sort.

major	mission	dozen	copper	carbon
senator	motor	thicken	latter	companion

/ən/ sound	/ər/ sound

Name ______________________________

Pattern Practice

common	remember	profession	bother
citizen	major	solution	differ

Write each word next to its synonym.

1. job ______________________
2. recall ______________________
3. important ______________________
4. contrast ______________________
5. answer ______________________
6. annoy ______________________
7. usual ______________________
8. resident ______________________

Write the word from sentences 1–8 that completes each sentence.

9. I can't ______________________ the last time we had this much fun!
10. Medicine is a ______________________ that requires years of training.
11. Any ______________________ of the town can vote on this issue.
12. The robin is a ______________________ bird in this state.
13. I would have called, but I didn't want to ______________________ you.
14. The hurricane is the first ______________________ storm of the year.
15. How do cats and dogs ______________________ from each other?
16. Please help me find the ______________________ to this math problem.

Use the Dictionary

Complete each word by adding *er, or, en,* or *on*. Check your spellings in a dictionary.

17. mirr__________
18. cinnam__________
19. diamet__________

Proofreading Practice

Read this report about Route 66 and find the mistakes. Use the proofreading marks below to show how each mistake should be corrected. Use a dictionary to check and correct spellings.

Proofreading Marks

Mark	Means	Example
℘	take away	America is made up ~~up~~ of many cultures.
∧	add	America ∧(is) made up of many cultures.
≡	make into an uppercase letter	america is made up of many cultures.
⊙	add a period	America is made up of many cultures⊙
/	make into a lowercase letter	America is made up of many Cultures.
(sp)	fix spelling	America is maade up of many cultures.

The Main Street of America

Route 66 is been called the "mother road" and the "main street of america." It represents adventure to many Americans'. The song "Get Your Kicks on Route 66" and a 1960s television series called "Route 66" are two examples of the role this road has played in popular culture.

Route 66 is one of the most famous roads in the world. When it was completed, it was more than 2,400 miles long and ran between chicago and Los angeles. Route 66 cross eight states and three time zones Before the Interstate Highway system was created, Route 66 was one of the most important roads linking the eastern and western parts of the United States.

In the 1930s, Route 66 carries many families from oklahoma to California. They farmland had been ruined by severely droughts in Oklahoma. Oklahomans desperate needed work and food. Many of them found work on farms in California. The Oklahomans called Route 66 the "Dust Bowl Hiway."

Today, Interstate 40 has replaced Route 66 as the main Route across Americas Southwest. But Route 66 is still a symbol of adventure, many people are sorry it has been replaced.

Name ____________________

Proofreading Checklist

You can use the list below to help you find and fix mistakes in your own writing. Write the titles of your own stories or reports in the blanks on top of the chart. Then use the questions to check your work. Make a check mark (✓) in each box after you have checked that item.

Proofreading Checklist for Unit 2

	Titles			
Have I capitalized proper nouns?				
Have I used plural and possessive nouns correctly?				
Have I used adverbs correctly?				
Have I used adjectives correctly?				
Have I used helping verbs correctly?				
Have I used coordinating, subordinating, and correlative conjunctions correctly?				

Also Remember…

Does each sentence begin with an uppercase letter?				
Does each sentence end with the right mark?				
Did I use a dictionary to check and correct spellings?				
Have I used commas correctly?				

Your Own List

Use this space to write your own list of things to check in your writing.

School Home Connection

In Unit 2 of *Grammar, Usage, and Mechanics,* students are learning about the different parts of speech, such as nouns, verbs, adjectives, and adverbs. The activities on this page give extra practice with some of the concepts students are learning. You can reinforce the information your child is learning in school by choosing one or more activities to complete with him or her at home.

Survey Says... **(Personal and Possessive Pronouns)**

Help your child conduct a survey. Together, list the names of family members on a sheet of paper. (Include friends and neighbors if you like.) Have your child ask the people individually whether they think the national anthem should be changed from "The Star-Spangled Banner" to "America the Beautiful" and why they think as they do. Have your child record each person's answer. Then have your child report the results to you, using personal and possessive pronouns in complete sentences. (Personal pronouns include *he, she, her, him, it, you, I, me, we, us, they,* and *them.* Possessive pronouns include *his, her, our, their, your, its,* and *my.*)

Example

My uncle thinks "America the Beautiful" should be the national anthem.
He thinks **it** is easier to sing than "The Star-Spangled Banner."

Word Search **(Adverbs)**

Work with your child to find at least fourteen adverbs in the puzzle below. (Adverbs tell *how, when, where,* and *how much* and often describe actions. Many adverbs end in *-ly,* but some do not. *Slowly, quickly, often, not,* and *never* are adverbs.)

B	F	U	L	G	E	N	E	R	O	U	S	L	Y
E	D	T	R	N	O	U	L	Y	C	P	Q	Q	D
S	S	M	K	O	N	L	Y	U	C	B	C	S	A
P	S	M	O	O	T	H	L	Y	A	P	U	L	N
E	F	F	O	R	T	L	E	S	S	L	Y	O	G
C	X	G	U	Z	L	A	Z	C	I	F	R	W	E
I	O	F	T	E	N	R	X	N	O	T	M	L	R
A	W	S	S	R	A	H	B	W	N	A	O	Y	O
L	M	N	I	H	V	A	L	W	A	Y	S	T	U
L	T	X	D	N	E	V	E	R	L	D	V	R	S
Y	R	A	E	N	I	T	K	U	L	W	S	C	L
L	Y	P	K	W	E	L	L	J	Y	M	O	L	Y

Now invite your child to use each adverb from the puzzle in a sentence.

Example

The whale swam **effortlessly** through the water.

Name ________________________________

River Wild (Action Verbs and Linking Verbs)

Ask your child to recall a river s/he has visited. Have your child write a few short sentences about the visit—two with action verbs and two with linking verbs. Work together to underline each action verb and circle each linking verb.

Example The Snake River flows through Colorado.

The water is cold throughout the year.

Mystery Guest (Main Verbs and Helping Verbs)

Ask your child to think of a member of your family or a close friend you both know. Invite your child to write five clue sentences to help you guess the mystery person. Ask your child to reveal one clue at a time, circling the main verb and underlining the helping verb in each clue, until you correctly name the mystery person. Then switch roles.

Example The person **has** **lived** in Wichita for fifty years.

The person **has** **visited** New York City many times.

Our Hero (Coordinating and Subordinating Conjunctions)

Work with your child to research an admirable American such as Frederick Douglass, Mother Jones, a past president, or someone else. Have your child write a few short sentences about the person. Work together to see how many pairs of sentences you can combine. Use coordinating conjunctions (*and, but, or*) or subordinating conjunctions (*since, if, because, when, although*).

Example George Washington Carver was a scientist. He was an artist. He was an inventor.

George Washington Carver was a scientist, an artist, **and** an inventor.

Example He is responsible for many inventions. He is best known for his work with peanuts.

Although he is responsible for many inventions, he is best known for his work with peanuts.

Silly Sentences (Plural and Possessive Nouns)

Give each player two index cards. Invite each player to write two nouns. (A noun names a person, place, thing, or idea.) One noun should be singular (*astronaut*) and one should be plural (*pancakes*). Put all the cards into one pile. Form teams of two people and take turns selecting two cards from the pile. Each team has one minute to come up with a sentence that includes both nouns and uses one noun as a possessive. (Possessive nouns, such as *girl's* or *women's*, show ownership.) Encourage the teams to make their sentences as silly as possible. Write all of the sentences on a piece of paper.

Example The **crocodile's shoes** were red.

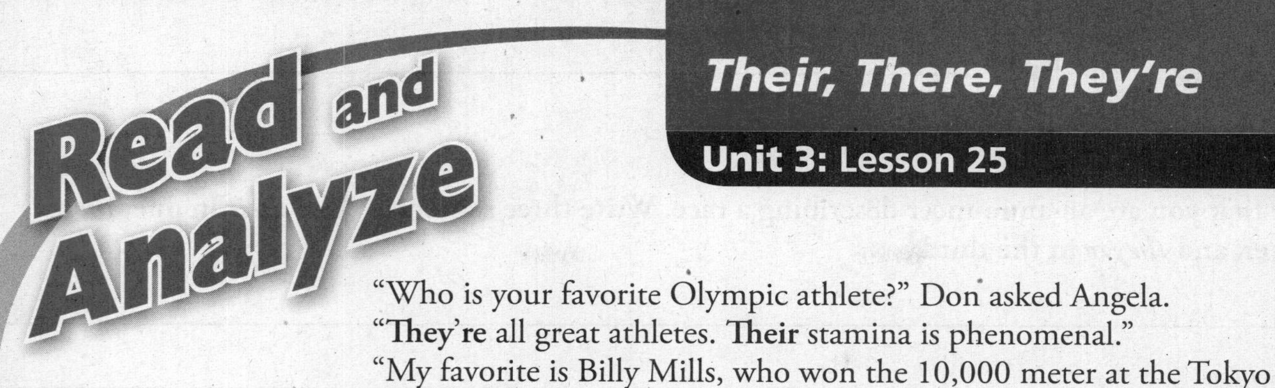

Their, There, They're

Unit 3: Lesson 25

"Who is your favorite Olympic athlete?" Don asked Angela.
"**They're** all great athletes. **Their** stamina is phenomenal."
"My favorite is Billy Mills, who won the 10,000 meter at the Tokyo Olympic games in 1964," said Don. "I wish I could have been **there!**"

Which boldfaced word means "belonging to them"? ______________

Which boldfaced word refers to a place? ______________

Which boldfaced word is a contraction of the words *they* and *are*? __________

The words **their, there,** and **they're** sound alike, but have different spellings and meanings. *Their* is a possessive pronoun meaning "belonging to them." *There* is an adverb that usually means "in that place." *They're* is the contraction made from the words *they are*.

See Handbook Section 28

Practice

Circle the word in parentheses that correctly completes each sentence.

1. "American spectators never thought (their/there/they're) countrymate could win," said Don.
2. "No American had ever won the 10,000 meter Olympic race before. (Their/There/They're) was an American silver medalist once, but that was back in 1912."
3. "The spectators must have been astounded," said Angela. "Who were (their/there/they're) favorites before the race?"
4. "(Their/There/They're) not so interesting to me," Don replied, "because those other runners had already won international medals."
5. "Here's how it happened," Don said, getting into the moment. "It's halfway through the race, and a few runners are ahead of the pack. (Their/There/They're) chasing Ron Clarke, the leader."

The movie *Running Brave* tells the story of Billy Mills.

6. "As they enter the last few laps, Mohammed Gammoudi pulls ahead. Clarke, then Mills, are right (their/there/they're) behind him. Then Mills begins losing ground."
7. "At the last minute, Mills sprints past both Clarke and Gammoudi to cross the finish line! People cannot believe (their/there/they're) eyes!"

Name ____________________

Apply

Imagine that you are an announcer describing a race. Write three sentences. Use *their* in one, *there* in another, and *they're* in the third.

8. ____________________

____

9. ____________________

____

10. ____________________

____

Reinforce

Write *their, there,* or *they're* in each blank. When you have completed the clues, solve the riddle. (11–19)

__________ made of valuable material, but __________ worth more than __________ weight in gold.

__________ are a limited number of them in the world.

They cannot be bought. In fact, __________ given away.

Every two years __________ is a chance to get one.

__________ owners hang them around __________ necks or on __________ walls.

What are they?

They're _ _ _ _ _ _ _   _ _ _ _ _ _.

Read and Analyze

Its and *It's*

Unit 3: Lesson 26

It's hard to remain at the top in table tennis. Jan-Ove Waldner has proven himself one of **its** most consistent performers over the past twenty years.

Which boldfaced word means "belonging to something"? ___________

Which is a contraction made from the words *it* and *is*? ___________

The words **its** and **it's** sound the same, but they have different spellings and meanings. *Its* is a possessive pronoun that means "belonging to it." *It's* is the contraction made from *it is* or *it has*.

See Handbook Section 28

Practice

Underline the word in parentheses that correctly completes each sentence.

1. To be successful in table tennis, (it's/its) helpful to begin playing at a young age.
2. By the time Jan-Ove Waldner was nine, table tennis had worked (it's/its) charms on him.
3. Jan-Ove studied table tennis in China, where (it's/its) a very popular sport.
4. He began winning championships as a teenager, and continued to win in his 20s and 30s; eventually the world of table tennis honored Jan-Ove as one of (it's/its) greatest champions.
5. Some say that athletic success comes from natural talent, and some say (it's/its) due to practice and desire.
6. Waldner says that to excel at a sport, you must practice (its/it's) skills.

Jan-Ove Waldner won two Olympic medals, one silver and one gold.

7. He tells table tennis players to work on hitting the ball on (its/it's) way up.
8. He says also to practice hitting the ball at the apex of (its/it's) flight.
9. (Its/It's) important to practice hitting downward-moving balls, too, in his opinion.
10. He says that (its/it's) particularly important to stay relaxed while competing.

Lesson 26

Name ______________________________

Apply

Write *its* or *it's* to complete each sentence.

11. When table tennis was first invented, _________ greatest appeal was that it could be played indoors.
12. Now ___________ one of the world's most popular sports, with more than 40 million competitive players worldwide.
13. In 1988 table tennis was awarded _________ status as a Summer Olympic sport.
14. Athleticism is a necessity for elite players, but ___________ not a requirement for casual players.
15. Children, older people, and disabled people can all play table tennis. ___________ recognized as an official sport of the Paralympics.

Reinforce

Write *its* or *it's* in each blank. Remember to capitalize a word if it begins a sentence. Then use the finished clues to solve the riddle. (16–24)

___________ an important part of the game, but ___________ not a player.

_________ job is at the table, but ___________ not an athlete.

___________ at every game, but ___________ not the property of either player.

___________ made of celluloid, the first plastic material.

___________ shaped like an eyeball, and ___________ just a little bigger than one.

What is it?

It's a table tennis _____ _____ _____ _____!

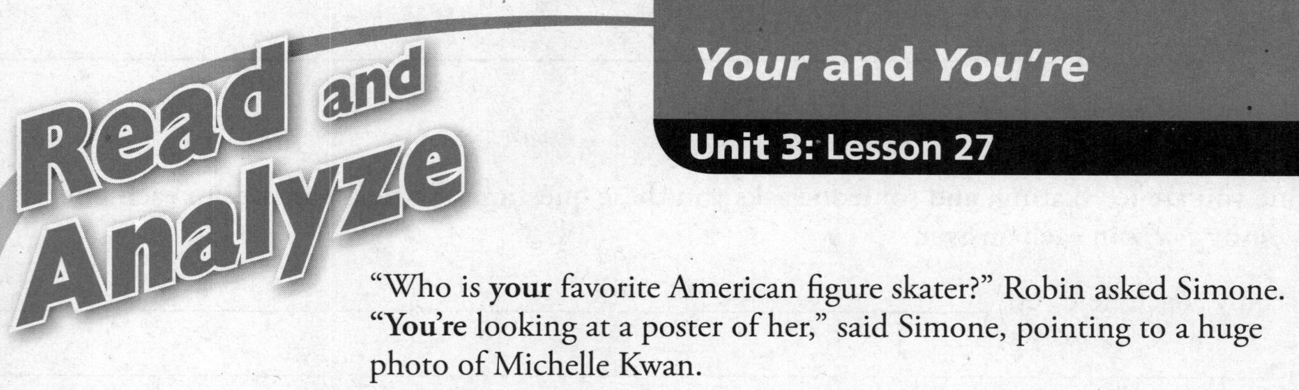

Your and You're

Unit 3: Lesson 27

"Who is **your** favorite American figure skater?" Robin asked Simone. "**You're** looking at a poster of her," said Simone, pointing to a huge photo of Michelle Kwan.

Which boldfaced word means "belonging to you"? ___________

Which boldfaced word is a short form of *you are*? ___________

The words **your** and **you're** sound the same, but they have different spellings and meanings. *Your* is a possessive pronoun. It means "belonging to you." *You're* is the contraction of the pronoun *you* and the verb *are*.

See Handbook Section 28

Practice

Underline the word in parentheses that correctly completes each sentence.

1. "I hear that (your/you're) an elegant skater just like Michelle Kwan," Robin said to Simone.
2. "I will never be as elegant as she is, but (your/you're) kind to say that," said Simone.
3. Robin asked, "If (your/you're) going to be here awhile, would you mind watching my routine?"
4. Simone asked, "Do they have (your/you're) music cued up?"
5. Robin nodded and said, "I think (your/you're) going to like it."
6. When Robin finished skating, Simone said, "(Your/You're) form has definitely improved, and the music is great."
7. "(Your/You're) friend Lili says you love Michelle Kwan's autobiography," Robin said.
8. "Oh, (your/you're) talking about *Michelle Kwan: Heart of a Champion,*" Simone answered.
9. She continued, "I have a copy signed by Michelle. (Your/You're) welcome to borrow it."
10. "I couldn't take (your/you're) copy; I'll borrow one from the library," Robin replied.

Michelle Kwan was a five-time world figure skating champion.

Name ______________________________

Apply

Imagine you are ice skating, and someone asks you these questions. Write an answer to each one. Use *your* or *you're* in each answer.

11. Is my coach here yet? ______________________________

12. Am I getting in the way? ______________________________

13. Did you find my coat in the dressing area? ______________________________

14. Am I starting my jump on the correct foot? ______________________________

15. Am I the greatest skater you've ever seen? ______________________________

Reinforce

Imagine you are the coach of a skater or another athlete who is about to compete. What can you say that will help him or her stay calm and perform well? What things should he or she remember? Write a pep talk you could give. Use *your* and *you're*.

Read and Analyze

Baseball fans love to argue about whether this star or that star is **better**, and who was the **best** player ever at a position. They also like to debate which of two bad teams is **worse** and which manager is the **worst** of all.

Underline the boldfaced words that compare two people or things. Circle the boldfaced words that compare more than two people or things.

The words **good** and **bad** change form when they're used to compare. Use **better** and **worse** when you compare two people or things. Use **best** and **worst** when you compare three or more people or things. Avoid *gooder, goodest, bestest, more better, worser, worstest, badder,* and *baddest*. These are all nonstandard forms. **Remember to use this information when you speak, too.**

See Handbook Section 23

Practice

Underline the form of *good* or *bad* that correctly completes each sentence.

1. Many people consider Ichiro Suzuki to be one of the (better/best) hitters of all time.
2. No hitter has ever had a (better/gooder) year than Ichiro had in 2004.
3. His total of 262 hits that year is the (bestest/best) single-year performance in major league history.
4. Ichiro also has the (best/most best) five-year hit total ever.
5. Unfortunately, his team at the time, the Seattle Mariners, had the (worse/worst) record in its division in two of those years.
6. Many players feel it's (worse/worst) to be an all-star on a losing team than to be a decent player on a championship team.
7. Ichiro would have a (worse/worst) batting average than he does if he did not have blazing speed.
8. His time from home plate to first base is (gooder/better) than most players'.
9. Ichiro uses bats of Japanese blue tamo wood, which he believes are (better/more better) than bats made of maple or hickory.

Ichiro Suzuki was the first non-pitcher from Japan to play major league baseball in the United States.

Name ______________________________

Apply

Write a form of *good* or *bad* from the word bank to complete each sentence.

best	better	worst	worse

10. The owner of the Brooklyn Dodgers, Branch Rickey, wanted only the ____________ players of all on his team.
11. He decided that baseball would be a much ____________ game with African American players than without them.
12. He signed Jackie Robinson to a contract because he thought Robinson was the ____________ person of all for the tough job of integrating the big leagues.
13. Robinson knew that being the first African American major league player would be hard, but his first year on the team was ____________ than he had expected.
14. Prejudiced fans called Robinson the ____________ names you could imagine.
15. Robinson had ____________ self-control than many other players, and he never let his anger show.
16. Robinson did the ____________ job he could despite the prejudice he faced.
17. Jackie Robinson was one of the very ____________ baseball players of his time, and he was certainly one of the bravest.

Reinforce

Compare baseball with another sport. Tell which one you like better and why. Use the words *best, worst, better,* and *worse.*

____

____

____

____

____

____

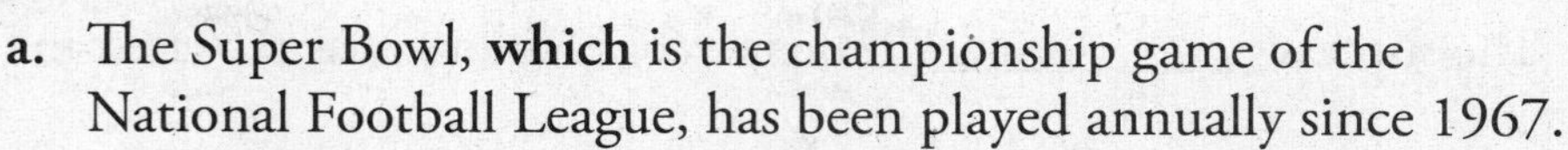

a. The Super Bowl, **which** is the championship game of the National Football League, has been played annually since 1967.
b. A quarterback **who** leads a team to a Super Bowl victory becomes famous for life.
c. Winning two Super Bowl championships is a feat **that** few quarterbacks have accomplished.

In which sentence does the boldfaced pronoun refer to a person? ______

Use **who** to refer to people. Use **which** to refer to things. You may use **that** to refer either to people or to things. Use *that* instead of *which* to begin a clause that is necessary to the meaning of the sentence.
Remember to use this information when you speak, too.

See Handbook Section 27

Practice

Underline the word in parentheses that correctly completes each sentence.

1. Quarterback is a position (who/that) demands leadership as well as athletic talent.
2. Jim Plunkett, (who/which) became a great quarterback, possesses both qualities.
3. Plunkett grew up in a household (who/that) was a bit unusual: both his mother and his father were blind.
4. His parents were people (who/which) believed that education should be a young person's top priority.
5. They told Jim (that/which) he had to study hard and do well if he wanted to play sports.
6. A high school athlete (who/which) competes in football, basketball, baseball, track, and wrestling is a rarity.
7. Jim won a football scholarship to Stanford University, (who/which) is an outstanding academic school.
8. In his senior year, Jim won the Heisman Trophy, the award (who/that) is given to the top college football player each year.

Jim Plunkett led the Oakland Raiders to victory in Super Bowl XV.

Name ______________________________

Apply

Write *who, which,* or *that* to complete each sentence correctly.

9. The success __________ Jim enjoyed in college was repeated in the pros during his first five years as the quarterback of the New England Patriots.
10. The team never reached the Super Bowl, though, __________ disappointed Jim.
11. In 1978 Jim Plunkett, __________ had been let go by his second team, the San Francisco 49ers, was signed by the Oakland Raiders.
12. Plunkett led the Raiders to the 1981 Super Bowl, __________ they won by a score of 27–10 over the Philadelphia Eagles.
13. Three years later Plunkett, __________ stepped back into the starting role in mid-year, led the Raiders to another Super Bowl win!
14. The impressive career __________ Jim Plunkett had as a quarterback earned him a place in sports history.

Reinforce

Complete the clues correctly by writing *who, which,* or *that.* Then answer the riddle. (15–19)

We are the targets __________ football kickers aim for.

A kick __________ sails through us adds to the score.

A kicker __________ sends balls through our uprights is a player who brings joy to the team's fans!

A conversion, __________ is worth one point, caps a touchdown.

But we prefer field goals, __________ are always worth three points!

We are the ___ ___ ___ ___ ___ ___ ___ ___ ___.

a. Mario Lemieux was **real** young when he began to play hockey.
b. He played on a **very** small rink behind the neighborhood church.
c. Everyone believed that Mario had **real** talent.

In which sentence is the boldfaced word used incorrectly? ________

Real is an adjective and must describe a noun or a pronoun. It means "actual." **Very** is an adverb. It means "extremely." Do not use *real* in place of *very*. **Remember to use this information when you speak, too.**

See Handbook Section 27

Practice

Draw *X* through each boldfaced word that is used incorrectly. Write *C* next to each sentence that uses the boldfaced word correctly.

1. In his **very** first season in the National Hockey League, Lemieux was chosen as the most valuable player in the All-Star Game. ______
2. He became a **real** hero throughout Canada in 1987 when he scored the winning goal in Canada's victory over the Soviet Union in an international championship series. ______
3. In the 1989–90 NHL season, Lemieux suffered a **real** painful back injury. ______
4. The next season, Lemieux led his team, the Pittsburgh Penguins, to their first league championship, symbolized by the **real** famous Stanley Cup. ______
5. In 1992, the Penguins again won the Stanley Cup, a **real** feat. ______
6. Then Lemieux faced a **real** challenge: he was diagnosed with Hodgkin's disease. ______
7. He missed a month of the 1992–93 season, but he played **real** well. ______
8. Later Lemieux missed almost two full seasons due to **real** serious health problems. ______
9. He surprised almost everyone by having one of his **very** best seasons when he returned. ______

Mario Lemieux was one of the greatest hockey scorers of all time.

Name ____

Apply

Write a sentence about each topic below. Use *very* or *real* in each sentence you write.

10. your favorite sport ____

11. why you like that sport ____

    ____

12. your favorite athlete ____

13. why you like that player ____

    ____

14. the most exciting sporting event you have seen ____

    ____

15. another topic that interests you ____

    ____

Reinforce

Complete this poem by writing *very* or *real* in each blank. Then answer the riddle. (16–22)

I'm __________ small and I'm __________ fast. If you close your eyes I'll shoot right past!

I live on the ice, where it's __________ cold. Or at least that's what I've been told.

I myself can't feel at all. I'm not a __________ player—I'm more like a ball.

Although I don't bounce, I'm perfectly round. I'm __________ important, though I stay on the ground.

I'm not __________ modest, but why should I be? I am hockey's __________ MVP!

What am I? I'm a ___ ___ ___ ___ ___ ___ ___ ___ ___ ___!

Read and Analyze

Set and *Sit*

Unit 3: Lesson 31

Tracy **set** her math books on the table. She **sat** down on the sofa and began watching a DVD of Olympic champion gymnast Carly Patterson.

Which boldfaced verb means "placed something somewhere"? __________

Which means "moved into a seat"? __________

Set and **sit** are different verbs. *Set* takes a direct object and *sit* does not. If you're about to use *set,* ask yourself, *"Set* what?" If you can't answer that question, use *sit*. Also, remember that you can't *sit* anything down—you must *set* it down. The past tense form of *sit* is *sat*. *Set* is spelled the same in the present and past tenses. **Remember to use this information when you speak, too.**

See Handbook Section 27

Practice

Underline the word in parentheses that correctly completes each sentence.

1. Carly (sat/set) her feet firmly on the balance beam.
2. Carly's fans in the bleachers (sat/set) silently and watched.
3. Her coach (sat/set) the clipboard on a chair and stared intently.
4. After she (sat/set) her hands exactly right, Carly slowly raised her body into a perfect handstand.
5. In the bleachers, Carly's fans couldn't (sit/set) still any longer.
6. They held their breath as Carly lowered her legs and (sat/set) her feet back on the balance beam.
7. Throughout Carly's routine, her coach (sat/set) on the sidelines, amazed by her calmness under pressure.
8. Carly (sat/set) her feet perfectly for her final move.
9. After her signature beam dismount, the young athlete (sat/set) down.
10. Carly (sat/set) quietly until the judges scored her performance.
11. In local, regional, and international meets, Carly Patterson has (sat/set) a new standard for gymnastic excellence in the United States.

Carly Patterson says the balance beam is her favorite event.

Name ______________________

Apply

Rewrite each sentence using a form of *set* or *sit* correctly. There is more than one way to rewrite each sentence.

12. The members of the audience at the 2004 Summer Olympics took their seats. ______________________

____

13. Gymnastic equipment had been carefully arranged in the arena. ______________________

____

14. Gymnasts from all over the world were in chairs on the sidelines. ______________________

____

15. Sixteen-year-old Carly Patterson was with the U.S. women's gymnastics team. ______________________

____

16. She always placed her feet perfectly in position on the balance beam. ______________________

____

17. By the end of the competition, Carly Patterson had a gold medal in the Women's Individual All-Around to deposit in her trophy case. ______________________

____

Reinforce

List three things you might set on a table. Then write three places you might sit down.

Things I Might *Set* Down	Places Where I Might *Sit* Down
______________	______________
______________	______________
______________	______________

Briana Scurry's parents **taught** her that she could succeed, but Briana **learned** for herself that success requires overcoming obstacles.

Which boldfaced word means "gained knowledge"? ________________

Which means "gave knowledge"? ________________

Both **learn** and **teach** are related to knowledge, so they are often confused. *Learn* means "to get knowledge" and *teach* means "to give knowledge." **Remember to use this information when you speak, too.**

Present	Past	With *have, has,* or *had*
learn(s)	learned	learned
teach(es)	taught	taught

See Handbook Section 27

Practice

Underline the word in parentheses that correctly completes each sentence.

1. At twelve years old, Briana (learned/taught) that there were no girls' soccer leagues in the Minneapolis area, so she joined a boys' league.
2. The coach (learned/taught) Briana to be a goalkeeper because he thought that was the safest position.
3. He soon (learned/taught) that Briana could take care of herself; the next three years she played in the field.
4. Then Briana became goalie again because she had (learned/taught) that she could control the game from there.
5. Briana (learned/taught) a lot in high school, where she played both soccer and basketball.
6. At the University of Massachusetts, coach Jim Rudy (learned/taught) her the fine points of goaltending.
7. After she graduated, she (learned/taught) that the U.S. Women's National Team wanted her.
8. From 1994 to 1999, Scurry started 95 international matches and posted 54 shutouts; she (learned/taught) the world how to be a great goalie.

Briana Scurry was a member of the gold medal-winning 2004 Olympic soccer team.

Name ______________________

Apply

Answer each question. Use the boldfaced word in your answer.

9. What do you want to **learn** in high school? ______________________

____

10. What important skill would you like to **teach** to a younger family member or friend?

____

____

11. What is the most important thing you have **learned** in the past year? ______________________

____

____

12. Think of a sport or hobby you like. What is the first thing a beginner should be **taught** about this sport or hobby? ______________________

____

____

Reinforce

Write a paragraph about something you learned from an important person in your life. Use *learn* and *teach* correctly.

____

____

____

____

____

____

____

____

____

Read and Analyze

Keilani Ricketts has led her team **to** victory in a college softball championship and has sparked teams to victory in **two** international competitions, **too**.

Circle the boldfaced word that means "also." Underline the boldfaced word that means "toward." Draw a box around the boldfaced word that means "one plus one."

Two, to, and ***too*** sound the same, but they have different spellings and meanings. *Two* is a number. *Too* means "also" or "more than enough." *To* often means "toward."

See Handbook Section 28

Practice

Circle the correct word in parentheses in each sentence. (1–10)

Keilani Ricketts experienced the best possible finish (to/two/too) her college softball career. She led her Oklahoma Sooners team (to/two/too) the NCAA national championship. Ricketts drove in all four of her team's runs to lead them to a 4–0 victory over the University of Tennessee in game (to/two/too) of the finals.

Ricketts had starred in game one of the finals, (to/two/too). She had pitched all 12 innings in Oklahoma's initial triumph over Tennessee. The national championship was number (to/two/too) for the Sooner women. They won the NCAA softball championship in 2000, (to/two/too).

Keilani Ricketts was named 2013 Player of the Year in NCAA women's softball.

In addition (to/two/too) her four years as an all-star at the University of Oklahoma, Ricketts has excelled in international competition, (to/two/too). In 2011 she led her USA Softball team (to/two/too) victory in the Pan American Games. In 2012, she pitched and won (to/two/too) games for USA Softball as they won the World Cup of Softball.

Name ____

Apply

Write *two, to,* or *too* to complete each sentence correctly.

11. Can a family have __________ much athletic talent?
12. Keilani Ricketts has __________ sisters, Samantha and Stephanie.
13. They are outstanding softball players, __________.
14. Like Keilani, Samantha went __________ the University of Oklahoma.
15. She was an All-American softball player there, __________!
16. Stephanie went __________ the University of Hawaii and played on their softball team.
17. Keilani's brother Richard won entrance __________ the United States Air Force Academy.
18. He played varsity sports, __________, but his sport was football.

Reinforce

Write a paragraph about a sport or an athlete. Use *two, to,* and *too* as many times as you can. Be sure to use each of these words correctly.

Read and Analyze

Irregular Verbs: *Know* and *Grow*

Unit 3: Lesson 34

Maritza Correia **growed** up near the ocean, so she **knew** how to stay safe at the beach.

Circle the boldfaced verb that is correct. Write the correct form of the other boldfaced word. ___________

Know and **grow** are **irregular verbs**. You cannot make the past tense of these verbs by adding *-ed*. These verbs have different forms.

Remember to use this information when you speak, too.

Present	Past	With *have, has,* or *had*
know(s)	knew	known
grow(s)	grew	grown

See Handbook Section 17

Practice

Underline the verb in parentheses that correctly completes each sentence.

1. When Maritza Correia was 6, doctors discovered that her spine had (grew/grown) curved.
2. If her parents had (knew/known) about her condition earlier, they probably would have acted sooner to correct it.
3. Correia's doctor (knew/known) that swimming could help, so Correia started to swim.
4. Her back condition improved, and she also (grew/growed) to be a strong swimmer.
5. Her skills (grew/grown), winning her medals at the World Championships in 2001, 2003, and 2004.
6. When Correia made the Olympic team in 2004, she (knew/knowed) she had made history.
7. Did you (know/known) that Correia was the first African American woman on a U.S. Olympic swim team?
8. Her reputation (grew/grown) when she won a silver medal at the 2004 Olympics.
9. She has swum so well that she has become (knowed/known) as "Relay Woman."

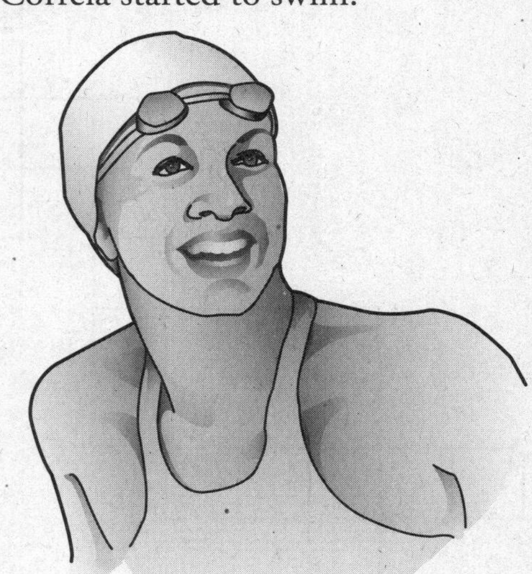

Maritza Correia overcame a physical challenge to become a champion swimmer.

Name ______________________________

Apply

Write sentences to answer the following questions. Use a form of *know* or *grow* in each sentence.

10. When did you first know you liked the sport or hobby that is now your favorite?

____

____

11. How does someone grow more and more skilled at that sport or hobby? ____________

____

____

12. How much have you grown in the last year? ______________________

____

13. How long have you known your best friend? ______________________

____

Reinforce

Use the correct forms of *know* or *grow* to complete the puzzle.

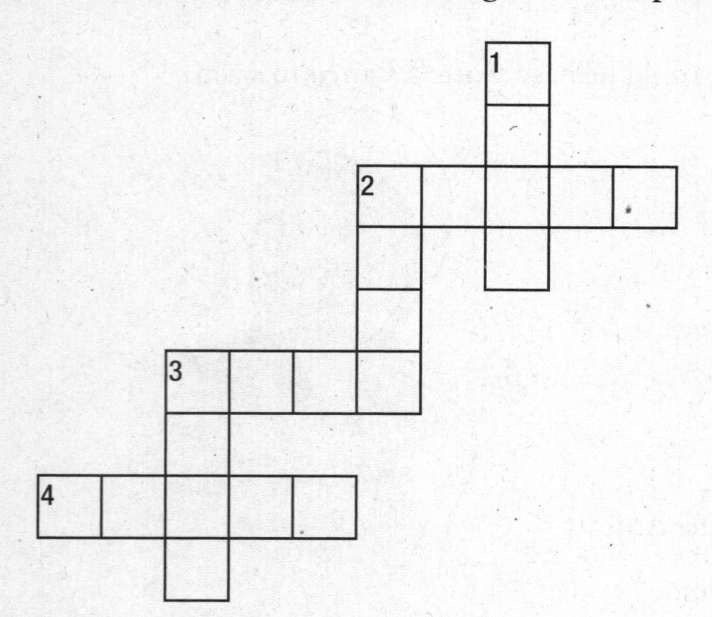

Across

2. "That girl has __ to be a fine athlete," said her coach.
3. "I always __ she would," said her mother.
4. "I have always __ that I wanted to be a swimmer," said the girl.

Down

1. "I want to get better as I __ older," she added.
2. She __ more confident as she won more and more competitions.
3. "I __ you will achieve your goals," said her coach.

Reflexive and Indefinite Pronouns

Unit 3: Lesson 35

Read and Analyze

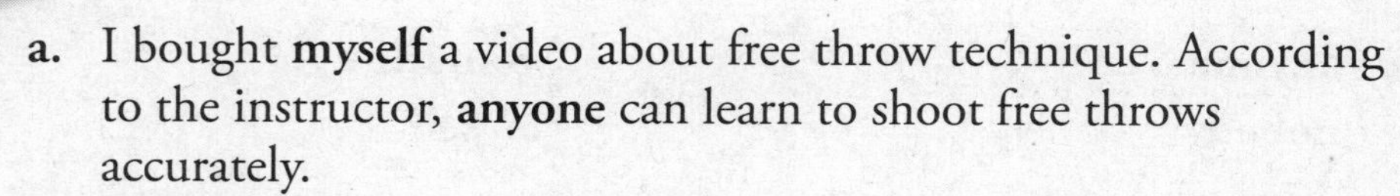

a. I bought **myself** a video about free throw technique. According to the instructor, **anyone** can learn to shoot free throws accurately.

b. I bought **me** a video about free throw technique. According to the instructor, **any one** can learn to shoot free throws accurately.

Look at the boldfaced words in each pair of sentences. Circle the letter by the sentences that are written correctly.

Myself, yourself, and *ourselves* are **reflexive pronouns**. A reflexive pronoun refers back to the subject of a sentence. *Anyone, nobody,* and *someone* are **indefinite pronouns**. An indefinite pronoun refers to one or more people or things not identified as individuals.

See Handbook Section 16

Practice

Read each sentence. Circle the word in parentheses that is the correct form of the pronoun.

1. My sister has taught (her self/herself) to relax before shooting a free throw.
2. She showed (me/myself) a video clip of Maya Moore, the WNBA all-star.
3. (No body/Nobody) looks more comfortable than she does at the free throw line.
4. (Every one/Everyone) else on my team made a higher percentage of free throws than I did last year.
5. I made (me/myself) a promise that I would work hard and improve.
6. The instructor on the video taught (himself/hisself) to shoot free throws after watching tapes of Steve Nash.
7. (Any one/Anyone) who is a real NBA fan knows that Steve Nash is the best free throw shooter in history.
8. My sister and I consider (us/ourselves) lucky.
9. Our family lives near a schoolyard with basketball courts, and there is almost always (some one/someone) to play with.
10. You can make (you/yourself) a more valuable player by working on your free throw technique.

Maya Moore is now among the best free throw shooters in women's pro basketball.

Name ____________________

Apply

Choose a word from the word bank to complete each sentence. Use correct capitalization.

anyone	yourself	ourselves
nobody	myself	themselves

11. You can help ____________ improve as a basketball player by working on your defense.
12. ____________ who wants to play good defense must keep a hand in the air at all times.
13. Players must remind ____________ to communicate with their teammates constantly.
14. ____________ who stands flat-footed can move quickly enough to stop a dribbler.
15. I constantly remind ____________ to stay between the player I am guarding and the basket.
16. We should always think of ____________ as team players!

Reinforce

Unscramble each pronoun below. Then write whether it is a reflexive pronoun or an indefinite pronoun.

slymef ____________ ____________________

boomsedy ____________ ____________________

shelfer ____________ ____________________

eyonever ____________ ____________________

shelmevest ____________ ____________________

Write two sentences using at least two of the reflexive pronouns and indefinite pronouns above.

____

____

____

Read and Analyze

Pronoun-Antecedent Agreement

Unit 3: Lesson 36

Bob Coomber is a record-setting wheelchair hiker. **He** has scaled White Mountain. At 14,246 feet, **it** is California's third-highest peak.

Circle the words that the pronoun *he* replaces. Draw a line under the words that *it* replaces.

An **antecedent** is the word or words a pronoun refers to. The antecedent is usually a noun. Sometimes it also includes words that modify the noun. When you write a pronoun, be sure its antecedent is clear. Pronouns must also **agree** with their antecedents. An antecedent and a pronoun agree when they have the same number (singular or plural) and gender (male or female).

See Handbook Section 16

Practice

Circle the antecedent for each boldfaced pronoun.

1. Bob Coomber's wheelchair is light and sturdy. With his strong arms, he can power **it** up rocky trails.
2. 4WheelBob, as **he** is known, also hikes on smoother, more level trails.
3. He and his wife spend time outdoors almost every weekend. **She** walks on two legs, and he rolls on four wheels.
4. Bob began using a wheelchair when **his** legs became too fragile to walk on as the result of complications from diabetes.
5. 4WheelBob writes a newspaper column for mobility device users. He tells **them** about trails they can move along easily.
6. In addition to White Mountain, Bob has climbed Mount Diablo, North Peak, and Mission Peak. **They** are three of the highest peaks in the San Francisco Bay Area.
7. 4WheelBob refuses to believe in limits, and he inspires others with disabilities to increase **their** participation in outdoor activities.
8. Bob Coomber received the President's Council on Physical Fitness Community Leadership Award in 2008. **It** was given to only 27 Americans in that year.

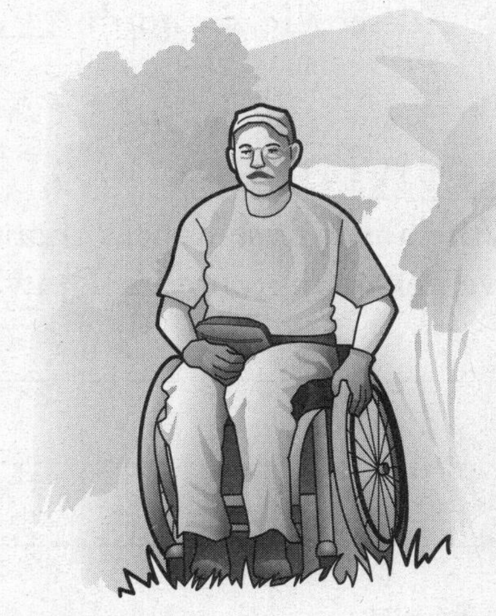

4WheelBob Coomber climbs mountains in his wheelchair.

 Name ______________________________

Apply

Write the pronoun that could stand for the boldfaced word or words in each sentence. Use correct capitalization.

9. **White Mountain** is located in eastern California. ____________ is near the town of Bishop.

10. **4WheelBob** had tried to climb that mountain before ____________ made his successful ascent, but altitude sickness had forced him to turn back.

11. To prevent a recurrence of the problem, **Coomber** camped for five days at 8,500 feet. This stay gave ____________ heart and lungs the chance to adjust to high altitude.

12. **Four friends** accompanied Coomber on his push to the summit. ____________ brought him water and supplies.

13. **Hikers** must bring water with ____________, because there is no water or shade on the trail to the summit.

14. Coomber needed three days to hike 5½ miles to the top of **White Mountain.** On ____________ slopes, Coomber saw a herd of bighorn sheep.

15. From the summit of White Mountain, **Coomber** could look out across 200 miles of Nevada desert. To the north ____________ could see 100 miles of snowy peaks.

Reinforce

Write a pair of sentences about someone you know who enjoys an outdoor activity. Use and circle two personal pronouns. Draw an arrow from each pronoun to the word or words it replaces.

____

____

____

____

____

____

____

Usage

Underline the word in parentheses that correctly completes each sentence.

1. The exhausted surfers stuck (their/there/they're) surfboards in the sand.
2. Then they sat down to catch (their/there/they're) breath.
3. "That was the (bestest/best) surfing I've done in weeks," said Alyssa.
4. "Not I," said Gustavo. "I did (gooder/better) yesterday."
5. "Look at that wave over (their/there/they're)!" Lani exclaimed.
6. "(It's/Its) at least twenty feet high!"
7. "A yacht would fit in (it's/its) curl!" she cried.
8. "Aren't you glad (you're/your) not out there?" Gustavo asked.
9. "Look at the lifeguards! (Their/There/They're) calling everyone in to shore," he continued.
10. "I (knew/knowed) it was a good time to quit," said Lani.

Write *who, which,* or *that* on the line to complete each sentence correctly.

11. Edson Arantes do Nascimento may be the greatest soccer player ______________________ has ever lived.
12. You may be more familiar with this star's nickname, ______________________ is Pelé.
13. It was Pelé's exploits as a member of the Brazilian national team ______________________ made him famous.
14. Soccer, ______________________ is popular throughout the world, is especially popular in Brazil.

Unit 3 **Review** Name ______________________________

Underline the word in parentheses that correctly completes each sentence.

15. If you want to learn to ski well, (you're/your) going to have to train hard.
16. First you must find a coach who will (learn/teach) you the right techniques.
17. It is also (real/very) important to eat a healthy diet.
18. Your training schedule won't leave you much time to (set/sit) on the sofa watching TV.
19. When your coach sees that you have (growed/grown) stronger and have developed good technique, you'll be allowed to compete in more challenging events.
20. Slalom racing is a (real/very) difficult event.
21. Slalom skiers are (know/known) for their strength, agility, and speed.
22. Bowling is a (very/real) popular sport.
23. Since bowlers spend much of their time (setting/sitting) down and waiting for their turns, this sport usually does not provide aerobic exercise.
24. My uncle wants to (learn/teach) me how to deliver a bowling ball correctly.
25. He (taught/learned) me to keep my eyes on the pins when I roll the ball.
26. (Two/To/Too) fun board sports are gaining popularity.
27. A wakeboarder holds tight (two/to/too) a tow rope and does tricks behind a boat.
28. A wake surfer uses a towrope, (two/to/too), but then drops the rope and rides the curl of the boat's wake.
29. Have you seen (anyone/any one) wakeboard or wake surf?
30. Wake surfers must keep (theirselves/themselves) balanced.
31. I might buy (me/myself) a wakeboard if I can save enough money.

Write the pronoun that could stand for the boldfaced word or words in each sentence. Use correct capitalization.

32. **My sister** is an excellent gymnast. ___________ does amazing moves on the balance beam.
33. **Her coaches** film her routines. ___________ post the clips on the team's website.
34. **My sister** watches the clips on ___________ computer.

Spelling Practice

The tennis champion has a quicker serve than his opponent. He is also the calmest person in the league. There's no denying that he's the one to beat!

Circle each word that ends with the suffix *-er*, *-est*, or *-ing*.

Adding Suffixes: *-er, -est, -ed, -ing*

The suffixes -er, -est, -ed, and -ing can be added to base words to form new words. There are rules to follow when adding these suffixes. If the word ends in a consonant and silent e, drop the e and add the ending (*late*, *later*). If the word ends in a consonant and *y*, change the *y* to *i* and add the ending (*funny*, *funniest*). In most cases, if the word ends in a vowel and one consonant, double the final consonant before adding the ending (*grin*, *grinned*).

Word Sort

Use the words below to complete the word sort.

removing	wiser	happiest	denied
trimmed	grayest	interesting	sunnier

Base word + *-er*	**Base word + *-est***
Base word + *-ed*	**Base word + *-ing***

Name ____

Pattern Practice

Add *-er, -est, -ed,* or *-ing* to each base word and write the new word.

1. wise + est ________________
2. slim + er ________________
3. supply + ed ________________
4. laugh + ing ________________
5. safe + est ________________
6. wide + er ________________
7. borrow + ed ________________

Add *-er, -est, -ed,* or *-ing* to the base word in parentheses to make it fit in the sentence. Write the new word.

8. Spain is the ________________ place in Europe. (sunny)
9. Aiden is ________________ the bushes in the front yard. (trim)
10. Mr. Slone ________________ the leaves from the pool. (remove)
11. Emma is ________________ than her older sister. (kind)
12. Brian ________________ that he had forgotten to meet me. (admit)
13. My family ________________ to Egypt to see the pyramids. (travel)
14. Mrs. Kirk needed help ________________ her groceries. (carry)

Use the
Dictionary

Write the base word for each word. Check your spellings in a dictionary.

15. excelling ________________
16. fluffier ________________
17. directed ________________
18. denied ________________

Proofreading Practice

Read this passage about bike tours and find the mistakes. Use the proofreading marks below to show how each mistake should be fixed. Use a dictionary to check and correct spellings.

Proofreading Marks

Mark	Means	Example
(delete mark)	take away	Riders climbs France's highest peaks.
^	add	Riders ^climb France's highest peaks.
≡	make into an uppercase letter	Riders climb france's highest peaks.
/	make into a lowercase letter	Riders Climb France's highest peaks.
⊙	add a period	Riders climb France's highest peaks⊙
(sp)	fix spelling	Riders climb France's hiest peaks.

Tour de France? Sure!

Nelson wasn't a professional cyclist. He was, like, a regular cycling enthusiast who happened to be sixty-one years old. Still, Nelson had just completed six days of the Tour de France bicling route.

Just hours ahead of the real Tour de France, nelson's tour group had cycled the same steep roads the professional riders would cycle later in the day. His tour group was made up of amateur cyclists which wanted to experience the challenges of the Tour de France.

The tour guides provided the hotels, meals, transportation, and medical support. The tour members even had they're own van following them, ready with food, advice, doctors, and, you know, a comfortable place to set down and catch a breath.

Do you think you'll ever want to ride in you're own Tour de France? By joining a group like this, nearly anyone can Anyone, that is, which can cycle a grooling 50 miles or more in a day, up and down mountains that are real steep. Do you think you might be interested? Then its time to start training!

Name ______________________________

Proofreading Checklist

You can use the list below to help you find and fix mistakes in your own writing. Write the titles of your own stories or reports on the blanks on top of the chart. Then use the questions to check your work. Make a check mark (✓) in each box after you have checked that item.

Proofreading Checklist for Unit 3

	Titles			
Have I used *your* and *you're* correctly?				
Have I used *its* and *it's* correctly?				
Have I used *their, there,* and *they're* correctly?				
Have I used *good* and *bad* correctly?				
Have I used *very* and *real* correctly?				
Have I used *sit* and *set* correctly?				
Have I used past tense forms of irregular verbs correctly?				

Also Remember…

Does each sentence begin with an uppercase letter?				
Does each sentence end with the correct end mark?				
Did I use a dictionary to check and correct spellings?				
Have I used commas correctly?				

Your Own List

Use this space to write your own list of things to check in your writing.

School Home Connection

In Unit 3 of *Grammar, Usage, and Mechanics,* students are learning how to use words that are often confused in writing, such as *its* and *it's.* The activities on these pages give extra practice with some of the concepts they are learning. You can help reinforce this information by choosing one or more activities to complete with your child at home.

Crossword Puzzle **(Irregular Verbs: *Know* and *Grow*)**

Work with your child to complete this crossword puzzle. Each missing word is a form of the word *know* or *grow.*

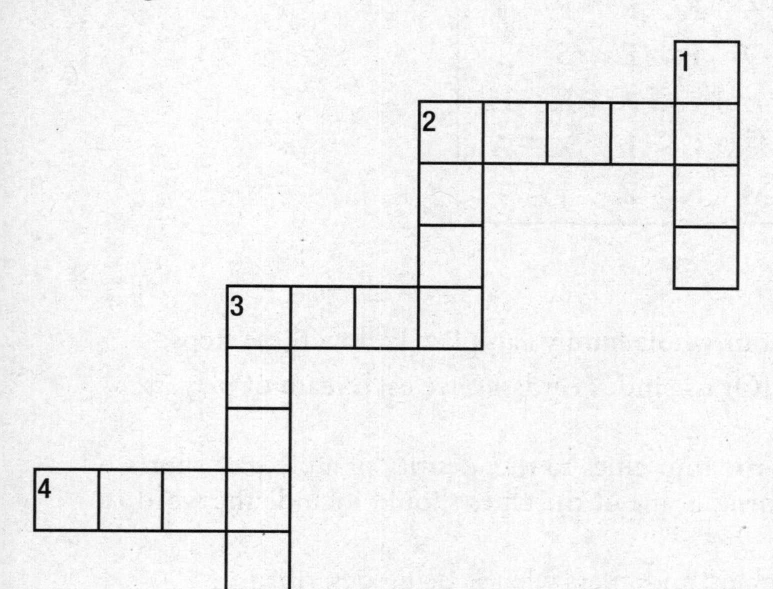

Across

2. Eli has __ stronger by doing exercises.
3. Even before yesterday's victory, I __ we'd win.
4. I __ more and more excited each time we scored.

Down

1. I __ it's not easy to become a professional soccer player.
2. When I __ up, I want to keep playing soccer on weekends.
3. I've __ for a long time that soccer is my favorite sport.

They're Over There with Their Sister **(*Their, There, They're*)**

With your child, write some sentences that describe family photos. Use the words *their, there,* and *they're* in your sentences. Have your child make sure each of these words is used correctly.

Example This photo shows Rosie and Eileen. **They're** my aunts.

In this photo, our family is posing with the Ortiz family and **their** dog.

Grab Bag **(*Its* and *It's; Their, There, They're; Your* and *You're; Too, Two, To*)**

You can play this game with several family members. Write these words on slips of paper: *its, it's, their, there, they're, your, you're, two, too,* and *to.* Put the slips into a paper sack. Take turns drawing a word and using it in a sentence. Ask listeners to decide which spelling of each word is being used in the sentence and how they know.

Name ______________________________

Word Search (Comparing with *Good* or *Bad*; *That, Which, Who*; *Real* and *Very*; *Set* and *Sit*)

There are 13 words hidden in the puzzle. Work with your child to find them all. Then ask your child to use each word in a sentence.

V	W	H	O	S	S	R	V	W
X	O	K	B	E	T	T	E	R
N	R	P	T	T	Q	C	R	P
R	S	Q	G	R	R	W	Y	S
G	E	W	O	R	S	T	Z	Q
K	M	Q	O	Z	K	R	P	J
F	B	A	D	Q	B	E	S	T
A	L	S	K	L	K	A	K	H
W	H	I	C	H	G	L	X	A
P	S	T	X	M	N	Z	J	T

Guessing Game (*Its* and *It's*)

Work with your child to create a guessing game your whole family can play. Follow these steps:

1. Cut thick paper into six 3" x 5" cards. (Or use index cards.) Give each team of players two cards.
2. On each card, team members should write four clues to the identity of a piece of sports equipment or one part of a sports uniform. Some of the clues should include the word *its* or *it's*.
3. Ask teams to exchange cards, read the clues, and guess what is being described.

1. It's made of wood or metal.
2. It's long and thin.
3. Its surface is smooth.
4. It's a little thicker at one end than it is at the other.

You might enjoy making up more categories, such as *animals, birds,* or *food.*

Read and Analyze

Subject and Object Pronouns

Auto racing fans admire the sleek cars before the race. **They** watch **them** closely during the warm-up period.

Which boldfaced word replaces the phrase *auto racing fans*? ___________

Which boldfaced word replaces the phrase *the sleek cars*? ___________

Which boldfaced word is the subject of the sentence? ___________

A pronoun can be the subject or the object in a sentence. **Subject pronouns** include *I, he, she, we,* and *they*. **Object pronouns** can be used after an action verb or a preposition. Object pronouns include *me, him, her, us,* and *them*. The pronouns *it* and *you* can be either subjects or objects. **Remember to use this information when you speak, too.**

See Handbook Section 16

Practice

Circle each boldfaced word that is a subject pronoun. Underline each boldfaced word that is an object pronoun.

1. My friends and **I** watch the Indy 500 every year on TV.
2. The speed, the noise, and the excitement thrill **us**.
3. **You** might know that only three drivers have four Indy victories to their credit.
4. Can **you** name **them**?
5. **They** are A.J. Foyt, Jr., Al Unser, Sr., and Rick Mears.
6. **I** have an autographed photo of Al Unser and his brother Bobby, another Indy winner.
7. My aunt Dinah gave **it** to **me**.
8. **I** keep **it** next to a photograph of Janet Guthrie.
9. Many fans remember **her** because **she** was the first woman to race at Indy.
10. Today more women are competing at Indy, and **they** are well prepared.
11. Indy competitor Sarah Fisher started racing a quarter-midget car when **she** was five.

Race cars are custom built for stability and speed.

Name ____________________

Apply

Rewrite each sentence. Replace each boldfaced phrase with a pronoun.

12. **Janet Guthrie** had to quit **the 1977 race** after 27 laps because of mechanical problems.

13. Sometimes **a driver's crew** can solve **mechanical problems** during a race.

14. **The crew** must often change **two or more tires** in just a few seconds.

15. **The driver** watches for **colored flag signals.**

16. **Safety** must be strictly maintained to prevent **accidents.**

Reinforce

Imagine that you were at an Indy 500 car race. Write two or three sentences about what you saw, heard, and felt at the racetrack. Use subject and object pronouns in your sentences.

Pronouns in Pairs

Unit 4: Lesson 38

a. Tyrin and me went to the drag races last weekend.
b. My cousin Phil introduced Tyrin and me to his racing partner, Betty.

If you remove "Tyrin and" from each sentence, which sentence sounds correct? ______

Use the pronouns *I, you, we, he, she, it,* and *they* as **subjects** in sentences. Use the pronouns *me, you, us, him, her, it,* and *them* as **objects** in sentences. **Remember to use this information when you speak, too.**

See Handbook Sections 16 and 27

Practice

Circle the correct pronoun in each pair. Write *S* if you chose a subject pronoun and *O* if you chose an object pronoun.

1. Betty and (he/him) take turns driving their dragster. ______
2. They showed Tyrin and (I/me) a picture of a dragster with an open parachute behind it. ______
3. Tyrin asked (they/them) why the parachute was there. ______
4. (She/Her) and Phil explained that parachutes help the dragsters stop after they cross the finish line. ______
5. Betty took Tyrin and (I/me) to the drag strip. ______
6. Phil took a picture of (she/her) and me standing in front of the dragster. ______
7. Then Tyrin and I watched Phil and (her/she) on their practice runs. ______
8. Phil told Tyrin and (I/me) that race car drivers need great concentration. ______
9. Now Tyrin and (I/me) want to learn how to drive a dragster. ______
10. (He/Him) and I will begin by reading more about drag racing. ______
11. Phil gave Tyrin and (I/me) a book about drag racing. ______
12. Tyrin and (I/me) can't wait to read it. ______

Some dragsters can travel over 300 miles per hour.

Name ______________________________

Apply

Rewrite the sentences. Substitute a pronoun for each boldfaced noun.

13. **Betty** and **Phil** drive a "funny car." ______________________________

____

14. A mechanic helped **Betty** and **Phil** build the car and perfect its engine. ______________________________

____

15. **Tyrin** and **Lorene** laughed when they heard the name of the car, Betty, Set, Go! ______________________________

____

16. Then Phil told **Lorene** and **Tyrin** that the car goes 200 miles per hour! ______________________________

____

17. Tyrin told **Phil** and **Betty** he wouldn't laugh anymore. ______________________________

____

Reinforce

Decide to whom each pronoun refers. (The answers appear in the sentences above.) Use the names to complete the puzzle.

Across

2. **She** drives a "funny car."
3. Tyrin told **him** he wouldn't laugh anymore.
5. Phil told **him** that the car goes 200 miles per hour.
6. **She** laughed at the name of the car.

Down

1. **He** helped Betty and Phil improve the car.
4. **He** laughed at the name of the car.

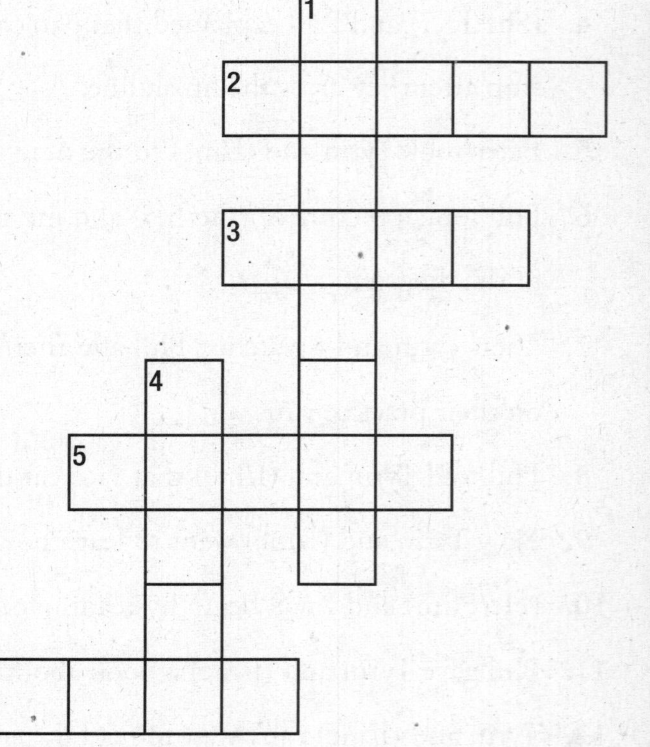

Subject-Verb Agreement

Unit 4: Lesson 39

Read and Analyze

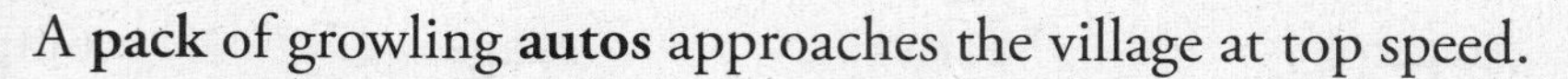

A **pack** of growling **autos** approaches the village at top speed.

Draw a box around the boldfaced noun that is the simple subject. Circle the boldfaced noun that is the object of the preposition *of*. Is the subject singular or plural? ____________________ Now underline the verb.

The **subject** and its **verb must agree**. Add *-s* or *-es* to a regular verb in the present tense when the subject is a singular noun or *he, she,* or *it*. Do not add *-s* or *-es* to a regular verb in the present tense when the subject is a plural noun or *I, you, we,* or *they*. Be sure that the verb agrees with its subject and not with the object of a preposition that comes before the verb. **Remember to use this information when you speak, too.**

See Handbook Section 17

Practice

Circle the simple subject in each sentence. Underline the correct verb in parentheses.

1. Many types of race cars (compete/competes) in races today.
2. Most experts (say/says) that Formula One cars are the costliest to build and race.
3. Engineers (create/creates) Formula One cars using some principles of airplane design.
4. A long, tubelike body and tires without fenders (make/makes) these cars easy to recognize.
5. Two pairs of wings attached to the car's body (keep/keeps) the car on the ground.
6. The downforce from the wings (enable/enables) the car to go fast around turns.
7. The engine (release/releases) much power to make the car move fast.
8. The engines (make/makes) a deafening roar.
9. People close to the track often (cover/covers) their ears.
10. Fans worldwide (follow/follows) Formula One racing.
11. Many fans (believe/believes) that Formula One competitions are more exciting than any other form of racing.

Some Formula One races are still held on roads and highways.

Name ____________________

Apply

Write a verb to complete each sentence correctly. You may use words from the word bank.

reach	earn	range	compete	win
reaches	earns	ranges	competes	wins

12. Formula One cars ________________ in a series called the Grand Prix.
13. Grand Prix races ________________ from about 150 to about 200 miles long.
14. The leader in a typical race ________________ speeds above 200 mph.
15. The top eight drivers to finish a Grand Prix race ________________ points.
16. At the end of the year, the driver with the most points ________________ the World Drivers' Championship.

Reinforce

Use the clues to complete the puzzle. Each answer is a verb that appears in this lesson.

Across

1. When the cars race by, I _____ my ears.
3. A boy in my class _____ money washing cars.
4. The driver of the car must _____ the parking brake before driving.
6. Winning this race will _____ him a champion.
7. The car in that showroom _____ speeds of 200 miles per hour.

Down

1. The woman in these pictures _____ in auto races.
2. Will the man in that car _____ the race?
5. A victory in this race will _____ him to enter the finals.

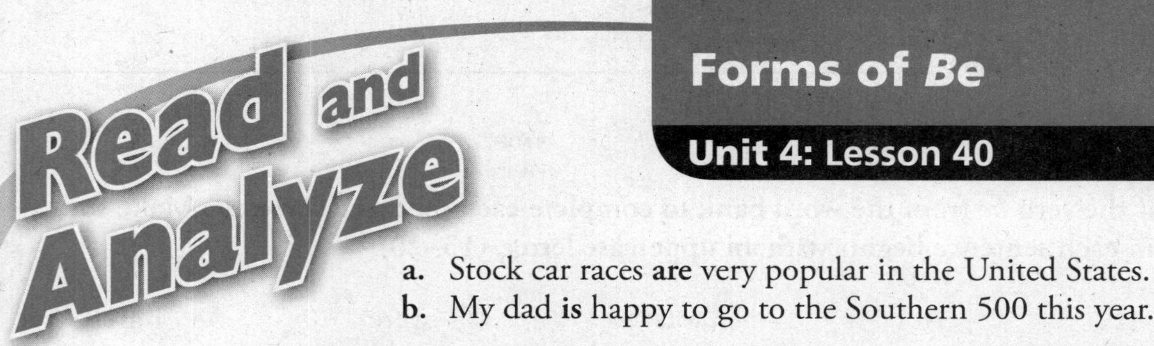

Forms of *Be*

Unit 4: Lesson 40

a. Stock car races **are** very popular in the United States.
b. My dad **is** happy to go to the Southern 500 this year.

Which sentence has a singular subject? _______ Circle the boldfaced verb in that sentence.

Which has a plural subject? _______ Underline the verb in that sentence.

Am, is, was, are, and *were* are forms of the verb *be*. Use *am* after the pronoun *I*. Use *is* or *was* after a **singular subject** or after the pronouns *he, she,* or *it*. Use *are* or *were* after a **plural subject** or after the pronouns *we, you,* or *they*. **Remember to use this information when you speak, too.**

See Handbook Sections 17 and 27

Practice

Underline the correct form of *be* in each sentence.

1. Stock car racing (was/were) first popular in the southern United States.
2. NASCAR (is/are) the association that governs stock car racing in the United States.
3. Once, only American cars (was/were) contestants in NASCAR races.
4. Today, cars of other nations (is/are) among the cars that compete.
5. Stock cars (is/are) similar in appearance to regular passenger cars.
6. Regular car engines (is/are) required in NASCAR autos.
7. However, a stock car (is/are) different from an ordinary car in many ways.
8. The car's engine (is/are) modified to make it more powerful.
9. The inside of the car (is/are) empty, except for the driver's seat and the controls.
10. Because stock cars have regular steel bodies, they (is/are) much heavier than most race cars.
11. The first NASCAR race (was/were) on a beach in Daytona, Florida, in 1948.
12. Today, the Daytona 500 (is/are) a famous stock car race.

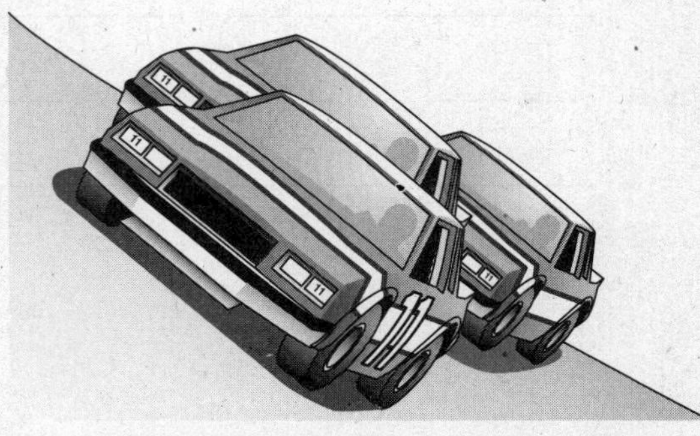

The banked corners of a stock car track help cars go around curves at over 200 mph.

Name ______________________________

Apply

Write a form of the verb *be* from the word bank to complete each sentence correctly. Make sure the first word in each sentence begins with an uppercase letter. (13–20)

am	is	was	were	are

__________ you at the NASCAR races last Saturday? I __________ there with my family. My sisters and I __________ big fans of car racing. My parents __________ fans, too. We __________ in the front row.

I __________ also a fan of drag racing. The races __________ very exciting! What __________ your favorite kind of car race?

Reinforce

Imagine that you and a friend are auto racers. Write five sentences about yourselves. Use a form of the verb *be* in each sentence.

21. ____

22. ____

23. ____

24. ____

25. ____

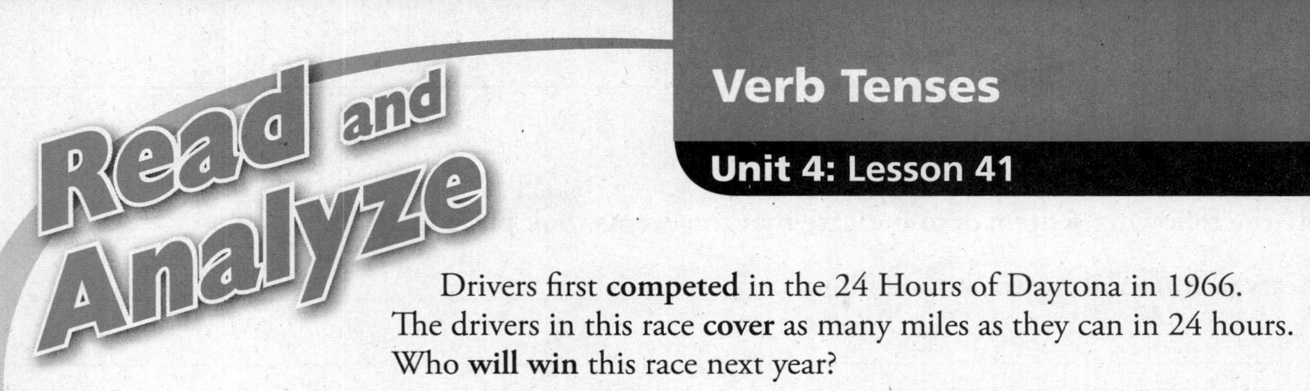

Drivers first **competed** in the 24 Hours of Daytona in 1966. The drivers in this race **cover** as many miles as they can in 24 hours. Who **will win** this race next year?

Circle the boldfaced verb that tells about something that will happen in the future. Underline the boldfaced verb that tells about something that already has happened. Draw a box around the boldfaced verb that tells about something that happens regularly or is true now.

A **present tense verb** is used to indicate that something happens regularly or is true now. A **past tense verb** tells about something that has already happened. A **future tense verb** tells what is going to happen.

See Handbook Section 17

Practice

The verb in each sentence appears in bold type. Draw a box around each present tense verb. Underline each past tense verb. Circle each future tense verb.

1. Until the 1960s, Ferraris **were** among the fastest race cars in the world.
2. In the late 1960s, Porsches **won** race after race.
3. Ferraris and Porsches still **compete** in auto races.
4. In 1970, Ferrari engineers **produced** an improved car.
5. A superior car **will win** a race only if it has an excellent driver.
6. The Ferrari team **chose** Mario Andretti as their driver.
7. Even today Andretti **is** famous for his driving ability.
8. Andretti **put** the new Ferrari to the test at Daytona.
9. To begin an auto race, the starter **waves** a green flag.
10. Perhaps someday you **will see** the green flag at Daytona.
11. Sixty-five cars **started** the race that year.
12. Spectators still **recall** Andretti's skillful handling of his Ferrari.
13. A Porsche **covered** more distance, though.
14. In 1972, Mario Andretti finally **drove** his Ferrari to victory at Daytona.

Name ______________________________

Apply

Rewrite the following sentences to indicate that the events took place in 1970.

15. Cars race around the track for 24 hours. ______________________________

16. Pedro Rodriguez drives the winning Porsche. ______________________________

17. Andretti finishes third in a Ferrari. ______________________________

The Porsche retained its racing crown at Daytona in 1970.

Reinforce

Write three sentences using the characters and verbs below. Use a different verb tense in each sentence. Check to make sure the verb tenses are correct.

Characters	Action Verb	Tense/Time
Laura, Polly	race	future
Zeon	watch	present
Ira	win	past

18. ______________________________

19. ______________________________

20. ______________________________

Read and Analyze

Progressive Forms of Verbs

Unit 4: Lesson 42

Vera and I **are going** to a demolition derby. We **will be seeing** dozens of collisions. Yesterday she and I **were watching** video clips of last year's derby.

Circle the boldfaced verb phrase that tells about an action that is going on now. Underline the boldfaced verb phrase that tells about an action that was happening for a while in the past. Draw a box around the verb phrase that tells about an action that will happen in the future.

Progressive forms of verbs show continuing action. To form a **present progressive** verb, add *am, is,* or *are* to the present participle of a verb (usually the present form + *-ing*): *is snoring*. To form a **past progressive** verb, add *was* or *were* to the present participle: *was playing*. To form a **future progressive** verb, add *will be* to the present participle: *will be ringing*.

See Handbook Section 17

Practice

Look at the boldfaced verb in each sentence. Circle each boldfaced verb that is a present progressive form. Underline each verb that is a past progressive form. Draw a box around each verb that is a future progressive form.

1. At half past twelve, the drivers **were starting** their beat-up vehicles.
2. Even now I **am remembering** the deafening noise and the pungent fumes!
3. "Which car **will** still **be running** at the end of the day?" Vera wondered.
4. Suddenly the announcer **was screaming** into his microphone.
5. "This derby **will be starting** in thirty seconds!" he hollered.
6. Vera **was explaining** that all parts which could injure drivers had been removed from the cars.
7. Within seconds after the starting gun, cars **were crashing** into each other!
8. "Some drivers **are going** backward!" I hollered to Vera.
9. "By ramming other cars with their rear bumpers, drivers **are protecting** their engines," she added.
10. "That blue Dodge **will be entering** the winner's circle," I predicted, and my prediction turned out to be correct!

Name ____________________

Apply

Use one or two helping verbs from the word bank plus a form of the verb in parentheses to complete each sentence. Each verb you write should be a progressive form.

am	are	was	will	be

11. Tomorrow at this time Betty and Phil ____________________ motorcycles at the raceway. (watch)
12. Betty and Phil ____________________ speeds in excess of 150 mph! (expect)
13. Last year my cousin ____________________ auto mechanics. (study)
14. I ____________________ that she would enjoy watching motorcycles race. (guess)

Reinforce

Answer each question in a complete sentence. Use at least one progressive verb form in each answer.

15. What were you studying in school at this time last year?

____

____

16. What are you studying in school now?

____

____

17. What do you expect to study at this time next year?

____

____

18. What activities do you hope to participate in next year?

____

____

Today **is** February 12, 1908. Six teams **have come** here to New York City for the greatest auto race in history!

Circle the boldfaced verb that tells about an action that began in the past and continues into the present.

The **present perfect tense** indicates action that started in the past and may still be happening. To form the present perfect tense, add the helping verb *has* or *have* to the past participle of a verb. The **past participle** of regular verbs is formed by adding *-ed* (*work/have worked*). Irregular verbs change their spelling when they form past participles (*build/have built*).

See Handbook Section 17

Practice

Circle each verb in the present perfect tense. Be sure to include the helping verb. If the verb is not in present perfect tense, don't mark anything.

1. This New York-to-Paris auto race has attracted worldwide interest.
2. Organizers have planned this race as a test of automobiles.
3. Perhaps it will be more of a test of drivers.
4. The first leg of this race has begun!
5. Drivers will race westward all the way across the United States, a distance of 3,000 miles.
6. Several days have passed since our last report.
7. Two French teams have quit the race.
8. They ran out of money.
9. All the remaining teams have become famous.
10. The American team is driving their car on the tracks of the transcontinental railroad!
11. The car's tires have popped from the rough ride.
12. The American, German, and Italian teams have crossed the Continental Divide.

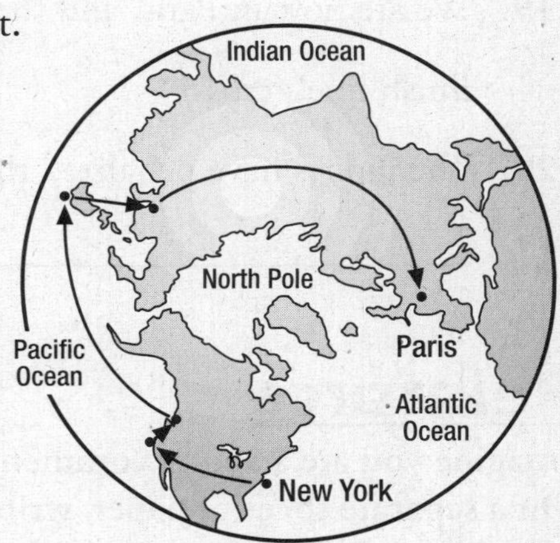

The 1908 race took drivers across three continents and 22,000 miles.

Name ______________________________

Apply

Write the present perfect form (*has* or *have* plus the past participle) of the verb in parentheses to complete each sentence correctly.

13. The German car ______________________ a breakdown here in Utah! (have)
14. The team ______________________ for the car to be shipped to Seattle by train. (arrange)
15. They ______________________ a race rule, and they may pay for this error later! (break)
16. The other teams ______________________ San Francisco and are now headed north. (reach)
17. The race organizers ______________________ the plan for how the cars will reach Russia. (change)
18. Instead of having the race cars drive across ice to go from Alaska, the organizers ______________________ that the cars will go by ship. (decide)
19. We are now in Paris, and the German team ______________________ the finish line! (cross)
20. The judges have penalized the Germans for breaking a race rule, and ______________________ the American team the winners. (declare)

Reinforce

Imagine you are a sports commentator posting live updates to the Internet on an exciting car race. On a separate sheet of paper, write a paragraph detailing the activity leading up to the big finish. Use the present perfect tense options from the word bank below.

has/have crossed	has/have passed	has/have charged
has/have switched	has/have sped	has/have won

Read and Analyze

By the time she finished high school, Elaine Larsen **had performed** as a cheerleader in front of crowds many times. As an adult she **has excited** audiences in quite a different way. In less than five minutes you **will have learned** what she does to thrill spectators.

Underline the boldfaced verb phrase that tells about an action that was completed by a certain time in the past. Draw a box around the boldfaced verb phrase that tells about an action that will be completed before a certain time in the future.

The **past perfect** tense (*had understood*) shows action that was completed by a certain time in the past. To form the past perfect tense, use *had* with the past participle of a verb. The **future perfect** tense (*will have affected*) shows action that will be completed by a certain time in the future. To form the future perfect tense, use *will have* with the past participle of a verb.

See Handbook Section 17

Practice

Underline each boldfaced verb that is in the past perfect tense. Draw a box around each boldfaced verb that is in the future perfect tense.

1. Shirley Muldowney and Janet Guthrie **had proven** that women could be excellent drag racers before Elaine Larsen began her racing career.
2. By the time she was 25, Elaine Larsen **had received** her dragster license.
3. Her husband Chris **had become** an expert welder and mechanic by then, and he later built a jet dragster for Elaine to drive.
4. Perhaps by the end of this year Elaine Larsen **will have set** a speed record.
5. If she is successful, she **will have used** all 6,000 horsepower generated by her dragster's powerful engine.
6. Until 2009 Elaine Larsen **had been** the only woman to drive one of Larsen Motorsports's jet dragsters.
7. Prior to that year, a young woman named Marisha Falk **had assisted** Elaine Larsen in a number of ways.
8. Thanks to Elaine Larsen, Marisha Falk **had earned** her dragster license by the time she was 26.
9. Maybe in a year or two Marisha Falk **will have exceeded** 300 mph in a jet dragster.
10. By the time Elaine Larsen and Marisha Falk have completed their driving careers, they almost certainly **will have attracted** other women to the world of jet drag racing.

 Name ____________________

Apply

Write the past perfect form (*had* + past participle) or the future perfect form (*will have* + past participle) of the verb in parentheses to complete each sentence.

11. Before I watched videos of jet drag racers, I ____________________ a career as an Indy car driver. (plan)
12. If I reach my goal, I ____________________ my dragster license by 2024. (earn)
13. Before the beginning of this year I ____________________ that aerodynamics would be too difficult for me to understand. (think)
14. By this weekend I ____________________ my third book about the aerodynamics of race cars. (read)
15. I ____________________ my science fair project about wind resistance by March 16, two weeks before the deadline! (complete)

Reinforce

Write a sentence about a goal you had chosen before you started school this year. Use a past perfect tense verb in the sentence. Then write a sentence about a time by which you will have achieved this goal (or will have set a different goal). Use a future perfect verb in the sentence.

____

____

____

____

____

____

____

____

____

____

Read and Analyze

Avoiding Inappropriate Tense Shifts

a. John wanted to know how to get involved in auto racing, so he sends an expert an e-mail asking for advice.
b. The expert responded to John's e-mail quickly and offered several positive suggestions.

Which sentence contains a verb that shifts the time frame in a way that doesn't make sense? _______ How should this sentence be rewritten so it stays in the time frame it established?

____

Choose **verb tenses** carefully so that the verb forms you use work together to indicate time accurately and consistently. When you describe events that happen in the same time frame, do not shift tenses. When you describe events that happen at different times, use verbs in different tenses to indicate the order in which the events happened.

See Handbook Section 17

Practice

Read each sentence. If the sentence contains a time shift that doesn't make sense, mark an *X* through the verb that makes the inappropriate tense shift. Then write the correct form of that verb on the line.

1. The expert writes an advice column for an auto magazine, and every month he chose a letter to answer. _____________
2. He answered John's letter in the May issue and tells John that the most important thing for him was to stay in school. _____________
3. The expert told John to study auto mechanics, because everyone needs to know how cars work. _____________
4. The expert has driven race cars for many years, and he has won many awards. _____________
5. The expert recommended that John go to auto races, and he advises John to buy a pit pass. _____________
6. According to the expert, drivers and mechanics will answer polite questions when they were not too busy. _____________
7. The expert also told John to consider becoming a go-kart racer and explained that racing stars such as Jeff Gordon and Tony Stewart drove go-karts when they were young. _____________
8. John read the suggestions with great excitement, and he immediately writes a thank-you message to the expert. _____________

Go-kart organizations teach young drivers how to race safely.

Name ______________________________

Apply

Rewrite the paragraph below to correct the inappropriate tense shifts.

From my seat I could see the mechanics working on the race car's engine. One mechanic holds a wrench and turned a bolt very slowly. The noise level was incredible! Then the crew chief suddenly gave a wave, all the mechanics jumped back, and the car roars back onto the track.

____

____

____

____

Reinforce

On the lines below, write a paragraph about the most exciting moment you've experienced at a sporting event. Start your paragraph with a description of that exciting moment. Then tell about what led up to that moment. Finally, tell what happened after the event. Choose verb tenses carefully so that the verb forms you use work together to indicate time accurately and consistently.

____

____

____

____

____

____

____

____

____

____

____

____

____

____

____

_____ Piero Taruffi hadn't never won the famous Mille Miglia.
_____ The Silver Fox didn't stop trying, however.

Write *X* in front of the sentence that has two negative words.

A **negative** is a word that means "no" or "not." The words *no, not, nothing, none, never, nowhere,* and *nobody* are negatives. The negative word *not* is often found in contractions like *don't* or *wasn't*. Use only one negative word in a sentence to express a negative idea.
Remember to use this information when you speak, too.

See Handbook Section 22

Practice

Write *X* next to each sentence with two negative expressions.

Mille Miglia **means "thousand miles" in Italian.**

1. Taruffi wouldn't never have another chance to win this race. _____
2. After 1957, the race wouldn't ever be run no more. _____
3. Racing experts thought Taruffi had almost no chance of beating the great British driver Stirling Moss. _____
4. Moss wasn't no threat after his brake pedal broke. _____
5. He wasn't in the race no more. _____
6. Late in the race, a young English driver named Collins held a large lead, but Taruffi would not give up. _____
7. Taruffi didn't never believe he would finally win the race. _____
8. "It wouldn't be so bad to come in second," he thought. _____
9. Collins had pushed his Ferrari too hard earlier, and it wasn't running well no more. _____
10. Taruffi flew past; he didn't have nobody in front of him. _____
11. There wasn't no one happier than the Silver Fox when he finally won the Mille Miglia after trying for so long. _____
12. His family and friends couldn't have been happier for him. _____

Name ________________________________

Apply

Rewrite these sentences correctly. There is more than one way to correct each sentence.

13. After 1957, the Mille Miglia wasn't held no more. ____________________

____

14. Fans along the racing route wouldn't never see the race cars zooming through their towns again. ____________________

____

15. Italian authorities had complained that there weren't no safety precautions.

____

____

16. They didn't want no fans to get hurt. ____________________

____

17. Anyone who saw the final race wouldn't never forget it. ____________________

____

Reinforce

Circle the hidden negatives and write them on the lines. Add apostrophes where they belong.

D	N	O	T	D	Q	P
O	D	B	Y	W	B	N
N	O	W	H	E	R	E
T	E	C	X	R	G	V
B	S	T	K	E	B	E
G	N	V	H	N	Q	R
D	T	B	Q	T	Z	K
Y	N	I	S	N	T	Y

18. ____________

19. ____________

20. ____________

21. ____________

22. ____________

23. ____________

24. ____________

Read and Analyze

Comparative and Superlative Adjectives

Lou was determined to create the **fastest** soap box racer in all of St. Louis this year. He needed to find a **more effective** type of axle grease than the one he had been using.

Circle the boldfaced adjective that compares something with one other thing. Draw a box around the boldfaced adjective that compares something with more than one other thing.

The **comparative form** of an adjective compares two people, places, or things. It is often followed by the word *than*. Add *-er* to short adjectives to create the comparative form. Use the word *more* before long adjectives to create this form. The **superlative form** of an adjective compares three or more people, places, or things. The superlative form usually follows the article *the*. Add *-est* to short adjectives to create the superlative. Use the word *most* before long adjectives to create this form. **Remember to use this information when you speak, too.**

See Handbook Sections 15 and 23

Practice

Think about how many things are being compared in each sentence. Then underline the correct form of the adjective in parentheses.

1. Last year, Lou had worked to make his car the (more beautiful/most beautiful) in the race.
2. He had used the (brighter/brightest) paints he could find.
3. He had used (brighter/brightest) colors for the sides than the top because a racer's sides are more visible than its top is.
4. When Lou and his friend Bill had compared their racers, Bill had admitted that Lou's was definitely (more colorful/the most colorful).
5. But Lou's pride faded when his car proved to be (slower/the slowest) of all the racers.
6. Lou knew he would have to work (harder/hardest) this year to build a better racer.
7. "Use (lighter/lightest) building materials than you used last year," said Lou's mom.
8. Lou decided to use a(n) (efficienter/more efficient) design for his new racer.
9. He was determined to build the (more streamlined/most streamlined) racer in the derby.

Name ____________________

Apply

On the blank, write the correct form of the adjective in parentheses. You will need to add *more, most, -er,* or *-est* to each adjective.

10. Soap box racers have no engine, so Lou had looked in hundreds of books to find the ____________ design. (efficient)

11. He had bought lightweight materials to make sure the new car would be ____________ than last year's model. (fast)

12. Today he would test his new car against Bill's car, the ____________ soap box racer in the neighborhood. (swift)

13. He thought his racer was the ____________ car in the world. (sleek)

14. For Lou, driving his newly designed racer was ____________ than beating Bill. (exciting)

Soap box races start on a downhill ramp.

Reinforce

Circle six hidden adjectives. If an adjective is a comparative, write its superlative form. If an adjective is a superlative, write its comparative form.

M	C	N	X	Q	C	S	S	C	H
L	D	G	J	T	B	O	J	P	I
S	N	T	K	X	D	F	K	M	G
W	I	L	D	E	S	T	N	G	H
V	R	O	C	R	H	E	L	K	E
N	Z	W	Q	B	S	R	D	B	S
J	K	E	A	R	L	I	E	S	T
X	S	S	P	K	N	L	J	P	G
P	T	T	F	A	S	T	E	R	K

15. ____________

16. ____________

17. ____________

18. ____________

19. ____________

20. ____________

Read and Analyze

Comparative and Superlative Adverbs

Unit 4: Lesson 48

The racers drove their midget race cars **more carefully** when it started to rain. Hank drove the **most carefully** of all the racers.

Circle the boldfaced adverb that compares two actions. Draw a box around the boldfaced adverb that compares three or more actions.

The **comparative form** of an adverb compares two actions. Adverbs that end in *-ly* are preceded by *more* for the comparative form (*more carefully*) and are often followed by the word *than*. The **superlative form** of an adverb compares three or more actions. Adverbs that end in *-ly* are preceded by *most* for the superlative form (*most carefully*). Some adverbs add *-er* for the comparative form (*faster*) and *-est* for the superlative form (*fastest*).

See Handbook Sections 18 and 23

Practice

Underline the correct form of the adverb.

1. After skidding on the first turn, Adrian approached the next corner (more cautiously/most cautiously).
2. Jayne drove the last lap (faster/fastest) than the first.
3. Kesara drove the last lap (more quickly/most quickly) than anyone else.
4. When Kesara crossed the finish line, her sister cheered (louder/loudest) of all.
5. Reza's midget car moved (more quickly/most quickly) than Anthony's car.
6. Tuan's engine ran (more smoothly/most smoothly) in the first race than in any other race.
7. Vera took the turns (more swiftly/most swiftly) than Reza.
8. Reza drives (most carefully/more carefully) than Vera.
9. Adrian drives (more cautiously/most cautiously) than Kesara.
10. Out of all the racers, Vera drives the (most boldly/more boldly).
11. Vera wins (more often/most often) than Reza.

Midget cars are very small race cars with very powerful engines.

Name ______________________________

Apply

Complete each sentence by writing the correct form of the adverb in parentheses. You will need to add *more, most, -er,* or *-est* to each adverb.

12. Vito's bright yellow car ran the ____________________ of all the midget race cars. (smoothly)
13. Kathy had thought she would be bored, but she ended up cheering ____________________ than any of her friends. (enthusiastically)
14. Now she is thinking that she could drive a midget car ____________________ than any driver on the track. (skillfully)
15. "After all, I ride my mountain bike downhill the ____________________ of all," she said to herself. (fast)
16. She watched the drivers ____________________ during the second race than she did during the first. (closely)

Reinforce

Write four sentences comparing the contestants in a competition you have recently seen. Use comparative and superlative adjectives and adverbs in your comparison.

17. ______________________________
____
18. ______________________________
____
19. ______________________________
____
20. ______________________________
____

Pronouns

Circle each boldfaced word that is a subject pronoun. Underline each boldfaced word that is an object pronoun. (1–4)

Barney Oldfield brought speed to racing. **He** was the first person to drive a car one mile per minute. In 1902 Henry Ford built a race car for **him.** Oldfield drove **it** in Detroit and won his first race in that car. In 1910 **he** set a world speed record of 131 mph.

Circle the correct pronoun or pronouns in parentheses.

5. Last weekend Grandma and Grandpa took my sister and (I/me) to the drag races.
6. They told (her and me/me and her) how they first became interested in drag racing.
7. She and (he/him) went to see Shirley "Cha-Cha" Muldowney race in 1969.

Verbs

Circle the correct form of each verb in parentheses.

8. "Shirley Muldowney (was/were) one of the first female race car drivers," Grandpa added.
9. "Many people (was/were) fans of Shirley," Grandma said.
10. "I still (has/have) articles about her performance at the 1971 Hot Rod Nationals in my scrapbook," Grandma said.
11. In the past I (collect/collected) toy race cars.
12. Now I frequently (sketch/sketched) race cars of my own design.
13. Tomorrow at this time I (was meeting/will be meeting) a race car driver.
14. This driver (was driving/is driving) a Porsche in races last year.
15. Right now she (is planning/was planning) to join a different racing team.
16. Before last Sunday I never (have expected/had expected) such a wonderful opportunity.
17. By next Sunday I (have talked/will have talked) with one of the most skillful race drivers in the world!

In each sentence, mark an *X* through the verb that makes an inappropriate time shift. Write the correct form of that verb on the line.

18. My brother writes a blog about auto racing, and every Friday he presented a summary of recent race results. ___

19. Last week I gathered information for my brother, and he uses it in the blog.

___

Negatives

Rewrite each sentence so it has only one negative term.

20. Great race car drivers never do nothing foolish. ___

___

21. None of them would never drive no unsafe car in a race. ___

___

22. On freeways, many drivers don't pay no attention to what they're doing. ___

___

Adjectives and Adverbs

Complete each sentence by writing the correct form of the adjective or adverb in parentheses.

23. A person who has a new car drives the ___ of all. (carefully)

24. Bruce's hot rod is ___ than his brother's sedan. (noisy)

25. After reading about different models, Gord decided that the new Remarka was the ___ car of all. (safe)

26. Gord believes the Remarka is ___ than the Afforda. (pretty)

27. He was surprised to learn that the Remarka handles ___ than the Afforda. (precisely)

28. Dan's car is the ___ of all. (quiet)

Spelling Practice

a. It is a good idea to have the brakes of your car inspected.
b. You don't want to be stuck on the road if something breaks.

Which sentence has a boldfaced word that means "stops working properly"?________

Which sentence has a boldfaced word that means "parts that cause a machine to stop"?________

Homophones

Homophones are words that sound the same but have different spellings and meanings, such as *waist* and *waste*. Homophones can be confusing. You will need to pay attention to the context of the sentence or use a dictionary to choose the correct spelling when writing homophones.

Words in Context

Write the word that best completes each sentence. Use a dictionary if you need help.

capitol	principal	coarse	vein
capital	course	principle	vain

1. The ________________ makes the school announcements each morning.
2. This scientific theory is based on one simple ________________.
3. The ________________ fabric of this shirt is uncomfortable.
4. It was a nice day to be playing on the golf ________________.
5. I could see the blue ________________ in her wrist.
6. A ________________ person is very concerned with his or her looks.
7. The state's ________________ building has a dome.
8. Topeka is the ________________ of Kansas.

Name ________________________________

Pattern Practice

Circle the homophone in parentheses that best completes each sentence.

9. My cat has gained too much (wait/weight) and needs to go on a diet.
10. Sara brushed her horse and put on its (bridle/bridal.)
11. Are you (aloud/allowed) to come to the movies with us?
12. Matt couldn't believe he forgot to put the (flower/flour) in the cake.

Write each homophone next to its meaning. Use a dictionary if you need help.

colonel	**kernel**	**pedal**	**naval**
through	**peddle**	**threw**	**navel**

13. ride a bike ____________
14. sell something ______________
15. related to sailing ____________
16. a physical feature on the stomach ____________
17. a military rank ________________
18. a grain of corn ______________
19. tossed something ____________
20. finished ________________

Use the
Dictionary

Complete each homophone pair. Check your spellings in a dictionary.

21. c__________mb__________l, a musical instrument

    s__________mb__________l, something that stands for something else

22. v__________ry, really

    v__________ry, to change

Proofreading Practice

Read this report about race car driver Kelly Sutton and find the mistakes. Use the proofreading marks below to show how each mistake should be fixed. Use a dictionary to check and correct spellings.

Proofreading Marks

Mark	Means	Example
⊙	add a period	Kelly Sutton is a NASCAR driver⊙
/	make into a lowercase letter	Kelly Sutton is a NASCAR Driver.
℘	take away	Kelly Sutton she is a NASCAR driver.
^	add	Kelly Sutton ^is a NASCAR driver.
(sp)	fix spelling	Kelly Sutton is a NASCAR dryver. (sp)

Kelly Sutton: NASCAR Driver

Kelly Sutton grew up wanting to be a race car driver. Like her grandfather and her father. When Kelly is sixteen, doctors gave her father and she some bad news. They said Kelly had multiple sclerosis, or MS. That disease attacks the nervous system most vigorously than many other illnesses do. People with MS may have trouble controlling their movements. The disease can get badder over time. Some people with MS must use wheelchairs

Kelly Sutton was determined to pursue her goals. She would not let nothing keep her down. She told her father she still wanted to drive a race car. She begins racing when she was nineteen years old. She proved herself to be a skillful driver, and she worked hard to get even better. Her determanation paid off. She became a NASCAR racer, just as her had hoped.. Sometimes she has to take time off because of her illness. As soon as she can, tho, she returns to the track.

When she isn't busy racing, Kelly helps other people with MS. She tells they about treatment options. She and them share experiences. Kelly want people with MS to know that they can make their dreams come true. Me and you can learn much from this inspiring person.

Name ____

Proofreading Checklist

You can use the list below to help you find and fix mistakes in your own writing. Write the titles of your own stories or reports in the blanks on top of the chart. Then use the questions to check your work. Make a check mark (✓) in each box after you have checked that item.

Titles

Proofreading Checklist for Unit 4

Have I used subject pronouns correctly? (*I, you, he, she, it, we, they*)				
Have I used object pronouns correctly? (*me, you, him, her, it, us, them*)				
Have I used progressive and present perfect tenses correctly?				
Do the subject and verb agree in every sentence?				
Have I used comparative and superlative forms of adverbs and adjectives correctly?				
Have I avoided extra negatives?				

Also Remember…

Does each sentence begin with an uppercase letter?				
Does each sentence end with the right mark?				
Did I use a dictionary to check and correct spellings?				
Have I used commas correctly?				

Your Own List

Use this space to write your own list of things to check in your writing.

School Home Connection

In Unit 4 of *Grammar, Usage, and Mechanics,* students are learning how different kinds of words are used in sentences. The activities on these pages give extra practice with some of the concepts they are learning. You can help reinforce the information your child is learning in school by choosing one or more activities to complete at home.

Guess What? **(Subject and Object Pronouns)**

Have your child think of an object that is familiar to both of you. Then have your child write three sentences about that object using pronouns; ask him or her not to tell what the object is.

Example   Aunt Sarah gave **it** to **you. You** wear **it** on your wrist. **It** ticks.

Read the sentences and guess what the secret object is. After you have guessed, work with your child to circle each pronoun he or she used.

Capture the Caption **(Forms of *Be*)**

With your child, flip through old magazines or a family photo album. Have your child select three or four pictures and write captions for them using forms of the verb *be,* such as *am, is, are, was,* or *were.*

Example   Grandma **is** in front of the piano. All the kids **are** in the kitchen.

Interview **(Pronouns in Pairs)**

Have your child interview you (or another adult) about what you did with your best friend when you were in the fifth grade. Encourage your child to take notes during the interview. Then have your child write four sentences describing what you and your friend did, using pronouns in some of the sentences.

Example   Mom and Greta were best friends.

She and Mom used to play on the soccer team together.

Read the completed sentences together to make sure the pronouns have been used correctly.

Name ______________________________

Silly Sentences (Subject-Verb Agreement)

Work with your child to think of three subjects, three verbs, and three locations. (Or, use the list below.) Write these in three columns, like this:

A bright red apple	roll	the sky
Three blue bikes	skid	the barn
The gray clouds	twist	the aisle

Then have your child choose one word or phrase from each column and write a sentence.

Example A bright red apple rolls down the aisle.

What's Wrong with These Pictures? (Negatives)

Look at these pictures with your child. Talk together about what is wrong with each picture. Then have your child use negatives to write one sentence about each picture. Make sure each sentence has only one negative word. Negatives include *no, not, nothing, none, never, nowhere,* and *nobody.*

Example The car has no tires.

Compare/Contrast (Comparative and Superlative Adjectives)

Have your child think of something that both of you have, such as a jacket, a closet, a hairbrush, or a bicycle. Then have your child write three sentences comparing the two things.

Example Your closet is <u>bigger</u> than mine. My closet is <u>messier</u> than yours.

In each sentence, have your child underline the word that compares.

Read and Analyze

Writing Sentences Correctly

Unit 5: Lesson 49

What is the largest turtle alive today? It is the leatherback turtle. Look at this picture of a leatherback. Wow, the caption says some leatherbacks weigh 1,400 pounds!

Which sentence gives a command? Draw a line under its end punctuation.
Which sentence shows excitement? Circle its end punctuation.
Which sentence asks a question? Draw a box around its end punctuation.
Which sentence makes a statement? Draw two lines under its end punctuation.

Begin every **sentence** with an uppercase letter. A **declarative** sentence makes a statement and ends with a **period**. An **interrogative** sentence asks a question and ends with a **question mark**. An **imperative** sentence gives a command and ends with a **period** or an **exclamation point**. An **exclamatory** sentence shows excitement and ends with an **exclamation point**.

See Handbook Section 9

Practice

Correct each capitalization or punctuation error. Then label each sentence *declarative, interrogative, imperative,* or *exclamatory*.

1. Tell me all about leatherback turtles? ____________________
2. Leatherbacks range over an extremely wide area ____________________
3. they can live in icy seas as well as tropical waters, ____________________
4. Why are they called leatherbacks. ____________________
5. These huge turtles do not have a hard shell! ____________________
6. How big is a leatherback's shell. ____________________
7. some shells are about six feet long? ____________________
8. do you know another way leatherbacks are unusual! ____________________
9. a leatherback can't pull its head into its shell. ____________________
10. Don't try to eat the leatherback's favorite food, the man-of-war? ____________________
11. These jellyfish are deadly to humans ____________________
12. Wow, the leatherback in that photograph is huge? ____________________

Name ______________________________

Apply

Look at the picture below. Write four sentences about it, one of each kind.

13. **Imperative:** ______________________________

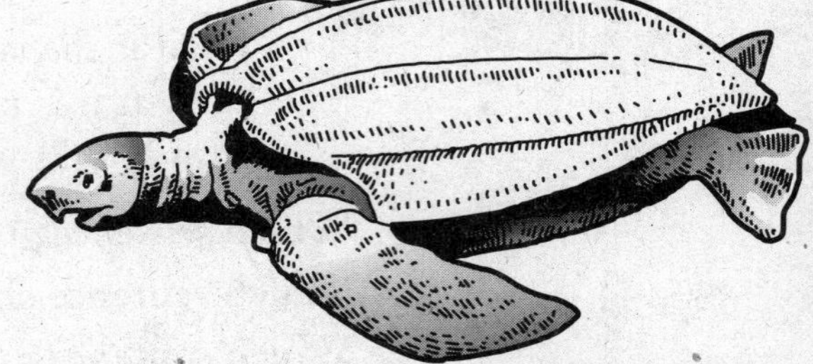

Leatherbacks have been found as far north as Norway and as far south as Australia.

14. **Interrogative:** ______________________________

____

15. **Declarative:** ______________________________

____

16. **Exclamatory:** ______________________________

____

Reinforce

Add end punctuation to each clue. Then solve the riddle.

17. I am round and smooth

18. Female sea turtles bury me on the beach

19. Please don't break me

20. I can't wait until a tiny turtle comes out of me

21. What am I

Answer: I am an _____ _____ _____.

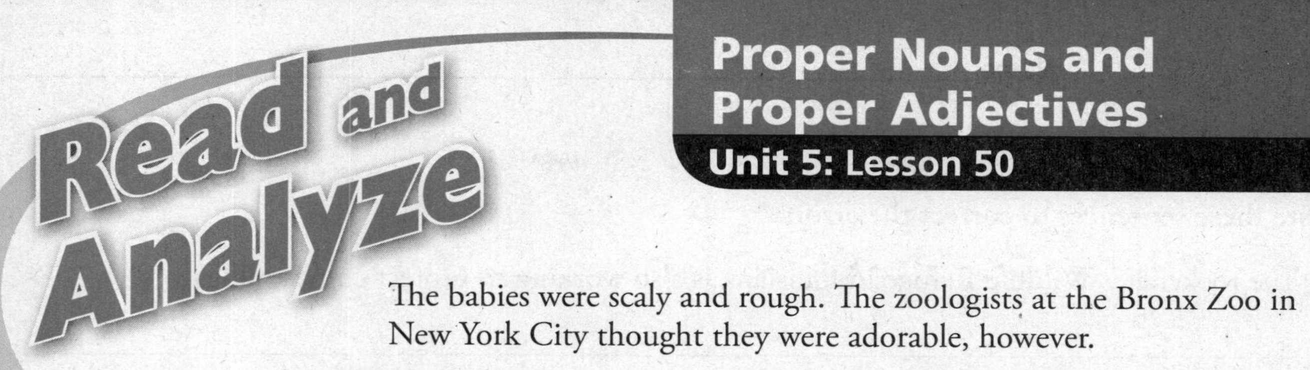

Proper Nouns and Proper Adjectives

Unit 5: Lesson 50

The babies were scaly and rough. The zoologists at the Bronx Zoo in New York City thought they were adorable, however.

Circle the words that name specific people, places, or organizations.

A common noun names a person, place, or thing. A **proper noun** names a specific person, place, or thing. All the important words in proper nouns are capitalized. The names of months and days of the week are proper nouns. **Proper adjectives** are descriptive words formed from proper nouns. They must be capitalized. A **title of respect** is used before a person's name. Titles of respect include *Chairperson* and *Mr*. They are also capitalized.

See Handbook Sections 1, 14, and 15

Practice

Circle lowercase letters that should be uppercase letters. Draw a line through uppercase letters that should be lowercase letters.

1. In the early 1980s, roughly 500 chinese alligators lived in the wild in china.
2. The Alligators' natural habitat in the Anhui province of china was being destroyed.
3. An american zoologist named doctor John L. behler wanted to help.
4. He brought chinese alligators to the bronx Zoo to create a breeding program.
5. On august 21, 1984, the Zoologist's effort finally paid off.
6. Four baby chinese alligators hatched from their shells.
7. The Zoo became the leader in captive breeding of Chinese alligators in the united states.
8. Another american reptile specialist, doctor myrna Watanabe, studied the alligators in China.
9. chinese officials and scientists worked hard to study and protect the Alligators, too.
10. Today there are about 10,000 Chinese alligators at a Research Center in anhui.
11. In april 2003, the bronx zoo sent three alligators to Shanghai to introduce into protected wetlands.
12. researchers were heartened when the Animals survived and one female had hatchlings.

Name ______________________________

Apply

Rewrite these sentences to correct the errors.

13. The rockefeller Wildlife Refuge in louisiana is also working to protect chinese alligators.

____

____

14. Parts of louisiana are like the alligators' home in the yangtze river in china.

____

____

15. Researchers in new york and louisiana work together to determine how captive-bred chinese alligators can be introduced into the wild.

____

____

Reinforce

Circle eight proper nouns, proper adjectives, or titles of respect. (All the hidden words appear in this lesson.) Write a sentence using two words you found. Use correct capitalization.

P	N	Z	D	Q	M	Y	R	N	A	C
R	S	Q	M	J	K	F	C	X	P	D
O	B	N	E	W	Y	O	R	K	R	O
B	A	M	E	R	I	C	A	N	T	C
E	C	H	I	N	E	S	E	U	D	T
H	P	K	S	E	W	K	S	W	V	O
L	T	Z	A	V	Q	X	K	G	J	R
E	L	O	U	I	S	I	A	N	A	Z
R	O	C	K	E	F	E	L	L	E	R

16. ______________________________

____

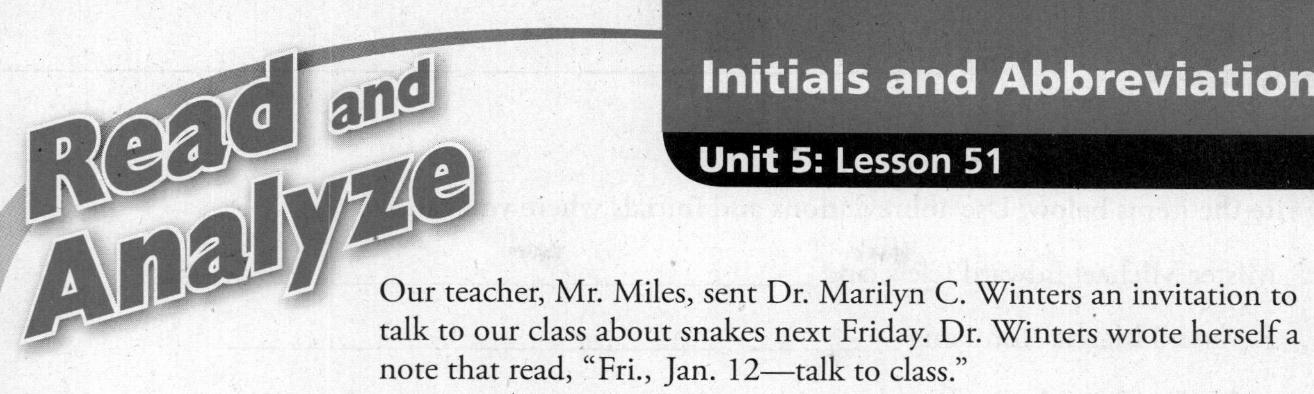

Initials and Abbreviations

Unit 5: Lesson 51

Our teacher, Mr. Miles, sent Dr. Marilyn C. Winters an invitation to talk to our class about snakes next Friday. Dr. Winters wrote herself a note that read, "Fri., Jan. 12—talk to class."

Underline a short way to write *Mister*. Draw a square around a short way to write *Doctor*. Circle short ways to write *Friday* and *January*. Underline a single letter that stands for a name.

An **abbreviation** is a shortened form of a word. **Titles of respect** are usually abbreviated. So are words in **addresses** like *Street* (*St.*) and *Avenue* (*Ave.*). Days, most months, and kinds of businesses are often abbreviated in e-mail and informal notes. Abbreviations usually begin with an uppercase letter and end with a period. An **initial** takes the place of a name. It is written as an uppercase letter followed by a period.

See Handbook Section 2

Practice

In the sentences below, circle each lowercase letter that should be an uppercase letter. Draw a line through each uppercase letter that should be a lowercase letter. Add periods where they are needed.

1. Mr Miles gave dr. Winters directions to u s Grant Middle School.
2. He told her to drive east on Elm Blvd and make a right on Oak st.
3. Dr Winters owns the most unusual business on Franklin ave.
4. Her company, Snakes inc, supplies snakes for films.
5. She showed us the feeding schedule for the boa constrictors.

   It read, "Feb Feeding Schedule: Feed boas every wed"

Boa constrictors use powerful muscles to squeeze and kill their prey.

6. Dr. Winters explained that she sometimes orders the food from Hungry Reptile corp.
7. She also feeds the boas mice from mrs Joy g Wong's pet store on Maple blvd.
8. Dr Winters said that boa constrictors do not lay eggs. Their babies are born live.
9. Mrs wong's assistant, ms Brown, had a big surprise last week.
10. When she got to the office on Franklin Ave, she found fifty newborn boas.
11. She told mrs. Wong, "I hope you have plenty of mice because we're going to need them!"

Name ______________________________

Apply

Rewrite the items below. Use abbreviations and initials where you can.

12. Mister Michael Edward Cleveland ____________________
13. Reverend Marcia Ann Fong ____________________
14. 1055 West Lincoln Boulevard ____________________
15. Reptile Research Incorporated ____________________
16. Tuesday, January 3 ____________________
17. Doctor Duane Estaris ____________________
18. today's date (include the day of the week) ____________________
19. your date of birth ____________________

Reinforce

Imagine you are addressing an envelope to your teacher. Write your teacher's name and the name and the address of your school. Then write your name and address in the top left corner. Check the capitalization and punctuation of the abbreviations you use in each address.

____
____
____

____
____
____
____

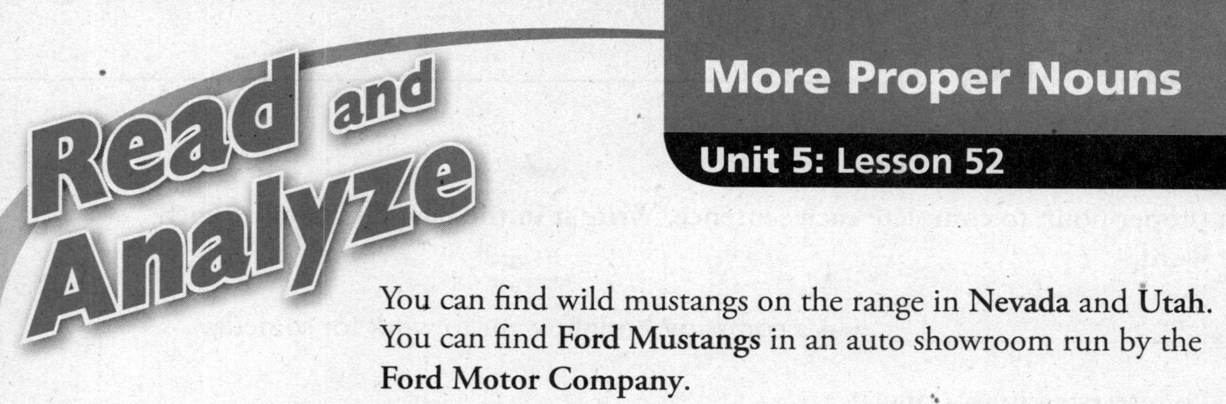

More Proper Nouns

Unit 5: Lesson 52

You can find wild mustangs on the range in **Nevada** and **Utah**. You can find **Ford Mustangs** in an auto showroom run by the **Ford Motor Company**.

Underline the boldfaced words that are the names of places. Circle the boldfaced words that are the name of a product. Draw a box around the boldfaced words that are the name of a company.

Proper nouns are the names of particular people, places, or things. Capitalize each important word in geographic names, important events, holidays, companies, and products.

See Handbook Sections 1 and 14

Practice

Circle each word that should begin with an uppercase letter.

1. Many auto companies in the united states have chosen animal names for their models.
2. The ford motor company, which has headquarters in dearborn, michigan, favors equine names.
3. In addition to the highly successful ford mustang, this company also has produced the ford bronco and the ford pinto.
4. Ford also manufactures mercurys, several of which have had feline names.
5. Have you heard of the mercury cougar, the mercury bobcat, or the mercury lynx?
6. These and other models of the mercury have been assembled in edison, new jersey, and wayne, michigan, as well as in canada and mexico.
7. Many years ago the hudson motor company produced cars with insect names.
8. The hudson hornet was one of the best cars of its day for both racing and everyday driving.
9. You can see both hudson hornets and hudson wasps at hostetler's hudson auto museum in shipshewana, indiana.
10. The museum is open tuesday through saturday most of the year, but it is closed from new year's day to april fool's day.

Name ______________________________

Apply

Think of a proper noun to complete each sentence. Write it in the blank. Capitalize each important word.

11. ____________________ is a company I might want to work for someday.

12. I'm also interested in working at ____________________.

13. One city I would like to visit is ____________________.

14. That city is in the state of ____________________.

15. One product our family uses and likes is ____________________.

16. The best holiday on which to visit our community is ____________________.

Reinforce

Write a paragraph about a type of store you would like to manage. Tell where it would be located and what products it would sell. Also tell when the store would be open and what holidays it would celebrate with special sales.

Titles

Unit 5: Lesson 53

Don't waste your money on the movie <u>Temple of the Turtles</u>.
The short story "Froggy's Fandango" is quite funny.
I used <u>The Reptile Encyclopedia</u> when I wrote my science report.

Circle the movie title. Draw a box around the story title. Tell how they are written differently. ______________________________

____

Underline **book titles** and **movie titles** in handwritten work. Italicize book titles and movie titles when you write with a word processor. Use quotation marks around the titles of **songs, stories,** and **poems**. Capitalize the first word and last word in every title you write. Capitalize all other words except articles, prepositions, and conjunctions. Remember to capitalize forms of the verb *be,* such as *is* and *are.*

See Handbook Sections 1 and 3

Practice

Circle each lowercase letter that should be an uppercase letter. Draw a line through uppercase letters that should be lowercase letters. Underline or add quotation marks to the titles.

1. Sagit lent Jorge a book called cobra capers.
2. Sagit thought spitting mad was the best story in the book.
3. Lu loved the movie the ghosts of rattlesnake ranch.
4. The movie's theme song is called spurs are jingling.
5. Mark Twain wrote a short story called the celebrated jumping frog of calaveras county.
6. After reading that story, Tran got the book teaching your frog to leap farther.
7. Nola wrote a poem called notes to a newt.
8. Brad set the poem to music, and he called the song amphibian rhapsody.
9. Joelle read the book the adventures of Leroy the lizard three times.
10. After dinner, Anya read us a poem from the book Odes to Toads.
11. The poem was titled a toad is a beautiful thing.
12. Then I read my poem titled A frog makes a Better pet than A hog.

Name ____________________

Apply

Read the titles below. Then write a title to answer each item. Be sure to write each title correctly.

13. Which book would tell you how to treat a snake bite? ____________________

____

14. Make up a title for a short story that might appear in Reptile Tales. ____________________

____

15. Which movie is likely to be a horror film? ____________________

____

16. Which book might give you information about painted turtles? ____________________

____

Reinforce

Draw a line to match each title in the first column with the item that best describes it in the second column.

17. "Ferdinand Frog's Life at the Plaza"	a movie about the life cycle of a turtle
18. Larry Lizard's Loud Act	a poem about a snake shedding its skin
19. "Marvin's Miraculous Molting"	a short story about a frog that lives in a fancy hotel
20. "Dot, the Silly Salamander"	a book about a singing lizard
21. The Life and Times of Tommy Turtle	a song about a spotted salamander

Read and Analyze

Apostrophes

Unit 5: Lesson 54

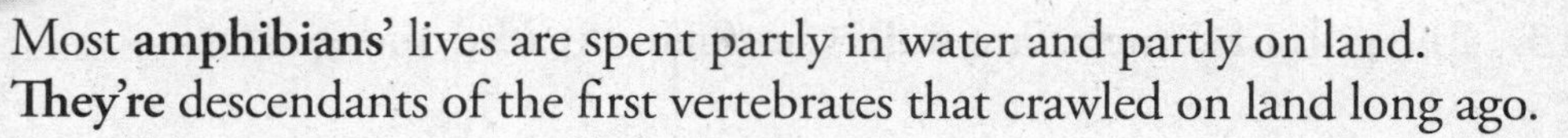

Most **amphibians'** lives are spent partly in water and partly on land. **They're** descendants of the first vertebrates that crawled on land long ago.

Which boldfaced word shows ownership? ______________________

Which boldfaced word combines two words? ______________

To form the **possessive** of a singular noun, add an **apostrophe** and -*s* (*snake's fangs*). For plural nouns that end in -*s*, add an apostrophe. For plural nouns that do not end in -*s*, add an apostrophe and -*s* (the *children's snake*). Apostrophes are also used in **contractions,** two words that have been shortened and combined.

See Handbook Sections 7, 24, and 26

Practice

Underline the correct word in parentheses. If the answer is a possessive, write *P*. If the answer is a contraction, write *C*.

1. (Ive/I've) read that amphibians stay the same temperature as their surroundings. _____
2. (That's/Thats') why we say they are "cold-blooded." _____
3. An (amphibian's/amphibians') body tells a lot about how it lives and moves. _____
4. Sticky disks on a tree (frogs'/frog's) fingers and toes help it grip and climb. _____
5. The spade-like shape of an African (bullfrogs'/bullfrog's) feet help it burrow into the ground. _____
6. Water (dwellers'/dweller's) webbed feet help them swim. _____
7. Some amphibians are colored to match their surroundings so that predators (won't/wo'nt) see them. _____
8. An (amphibian's/amphibians') color may help it stay warm or cool. _____
9. A (tadpole's/tadpoles') form changes as it grows into a frog. _____
10. Tadpoles (don't/do'nt) breathe air. _____
11. They (cant/can't) live out of water until they have changed form and become frogs. _____
12. Frogs (don't/dont) flip out their tongues at their prey unless the prey is moving. _____

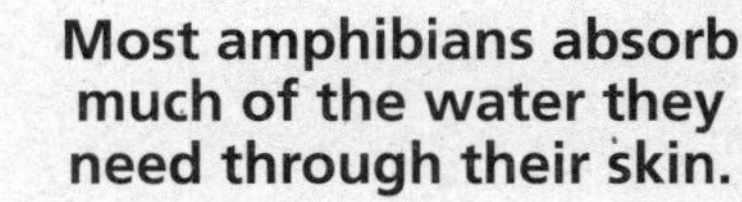

Most amphibians absorb much of the water they need through their skin.

Name ______________________________

Apply

Rewrite the sentences below. Replace the boldfaced words with possessives or contractions.

13. The **gills of some salamanders** let them breathe underwater. ______________________________

____

14. **Do not** expect a short-legged frog to make long jumps. ______________________________

____

15. The **skin color of a poison-dart frog** warns other creatures to stay away. ______________________________

____

16. **It is** a little known fact that some amphibians have no legs. ______________________________

____

17. **They are** called caecilians, and they look like worms. ______________________________

____

Reinforce

Circle the five hidden words in the puzzle. Then write the possessive form of each noun and the contraction of the negative expression. (Hint: Two of the nouns are plural.)

Y	D	L	T	A	D	P	O	L	E
W	C	K	X	G	M	B	S	K	F
S	A	L	A	M	A	N	D	E	R
Q	N	B	J	M	K	Q	F	B	O
X	N	G	U	S	S	E	R	P	G
Z	O	X	K	J	G	N	V	R	S
V	T	O	N	G	U	E	S	D	B

18. ______________________________

19. ______________________________

20. ______________________________

21. ______________________________

22. ______________________________

Read and Analyze

Uses of Commas

Unit 5: Lesson 55

Salamanders may look like lizards, geckos, or even snakes.

In the sentence above, circle three items in a series. What punctuation mark follows each of the first two items? ____________________

Well, salamanders are not related to any of those creatures.

In the sentence above, circle the introductory word that expresses an emotion and is not part of the independent clause that follows it. What punctuation mark separates the word from the rest of the sentence?

____

A **series** is a list of three or more words or phrases. **Commas** are used to separate the items in a series. The last comma in a series goes before the conjunction *and* or *or*. A comma is also used to separate a mild **interjection** at the beginning of a sentence from the rest of the sentence.

See Handbook Section 8

Practice

Add commas where they are needed below. Cross out commas that should not appear. Circle each interjection.

1. Hey salamanders are actually related to frogs, toads and other amphibians.
2. An adult spotted salamander has, four legs a tail, black skin and yellow spots.
3. Spotted salamanders, hatch mate, and lay eggs underwater.
4. A female lays her eggs attaches them to a stick, covers them with a jelly-like substance and, leaves them.
5. Grubs mold or acid rain, can kill the salamander eggs.
6. The spotted salamander larvae, eat fleas shrimps and grubs.
7. Beetles, salamanders or giant water bugs might eat, the larvae.
8. As adults, the spotted salamanders leave the pool crawl on land and find hiding places.
9. Adult spotted salamanders live under rocks, in holes or, in rotten logs.
10. Oh I just found a salamander's hiding place!

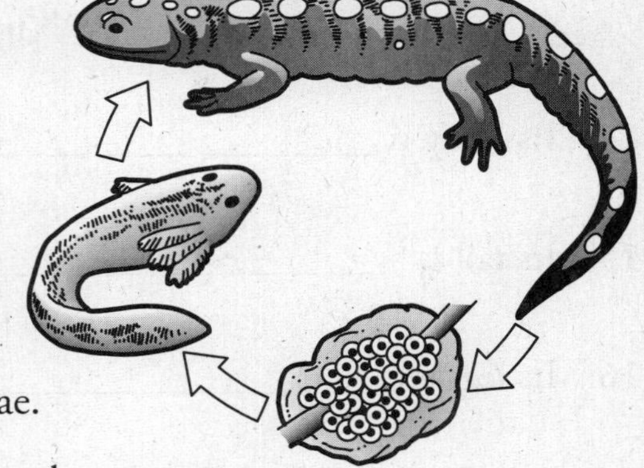

The life cycle of the spotted salamander

Lesson 55

Name ______________________________

Apply

Use what you read on page 147 to write a sentence to respond to each item. Include items in a series in each answer.

11. List three creatures that spotted salamander larvae eat.

____

____

12. List three places where you might find a spotted salamander.

____

____

13. List three dangers for spotted salamander eggs and larvae.

____

____

Reinforce

Imagine that you have discovered a new species of salamander. Complete the sentences below to describe your salamander. Use at least three adjectives in each answer. (Use words from the word bank or your own words.) Be sure to use commas correctly. Also, add an interjection to one of your sentences. Then draw your salamander.

green	long	striped	bumpy	spotted	wrinkled
red	smooth	slimy	yellow	shiny	short

14. Its body is ______________________________

15. Its tail is ______________________________

16. Its legs are ______________________________

Read and Analyze

More Uses of Commas

Unit 5: Lesson 56

Yes, we decided to have a frog jumping contest. Ms. Li helped us catch the bullfrogs, but she said that we'd have to let them go later. "Celia, I asked you to handle your frog carefully, didn't I?" said Ms. Li.

Find the word that introduces the first sentence. What punctuation mark follows it? ____________

Find the conjunction that joins the two parts of the second sentence. What punctuation mark comes before it? ____________

Find the name of the person being spoken to in the third sentence. What punctuation mark comes after it? ____________

Find the question that is tagged onto the end of the sentence in quotation marks. What punctuation mark comes before it? ____________

Commas tell a reader where to pause. A comma is also used to separate an **introductory word** such as *yes* or *no*, an **introductory element**, a **noun of direct address**, or a **tag question** from the rest of a sentence. A comma is also used to separate the **independent clauses** in a compound sentence.

See Handbook Sections 8 and 21

Practice

A comma is missing from each sentence. Add the missing comma. Then decide why each comma is needed. Write *I* for introductory word or element, *D* for direct address, *T* for tag question, or *C* for compound sentence.

1. "Ms. Li what species of frog is the best jumper?" asked Ken. _____
2. "Ken the African sharp-nosed frog can jump 65 times its body length," she said. _____
3. "Its legs are really long aren't they?" asked Ray. _____
4. Ms. Li said, "Yes frogs' powerful legs make them good jumpers." _____
5. "Do you know another way frogs use their legs Ali?" Ms. Li asked. _____
6. "Yes they use them to swim," Ali answered. _____
7. "Many frogs have webbed feet and that helps them swim faster." _____
8. Because we were studying frogs we had a frog race. _____
9. "Follow that frog will you?" Jenny shouted at Raj. _____
10. Ms. Li gave the signal and we urged our frogs to jump. _____

Bullfrogs can jump up to nine times the length of their bodies.

Lesson 56

Name ______________________________

Apply

Rewrite the sentences so they include the word or words in parentheses. Be sure to use commas correctly.

11. Some frogs live near water. (and) Others are tree dwellers. ______________________________

____

12. Many frogs capture insects with their long, sticky tongues. (but) Others gulp food directly into their mouths.

____

____

13. Put your frog back in the pond. (James) ______________________________

____

14. The frog will be happier there. (won't it) ______________________________

____

Reinforce

Amphibians can live on land or in water. The words *amphibian* and *amphibious* come from two Greek roots: *amphi,* meaning "both," and *bios,* meaning "life." Write a paragraph explaining how amphibians live a double life. Use commas to separate elements in your sentences.

____

____

____

____

____

____

____

____

____

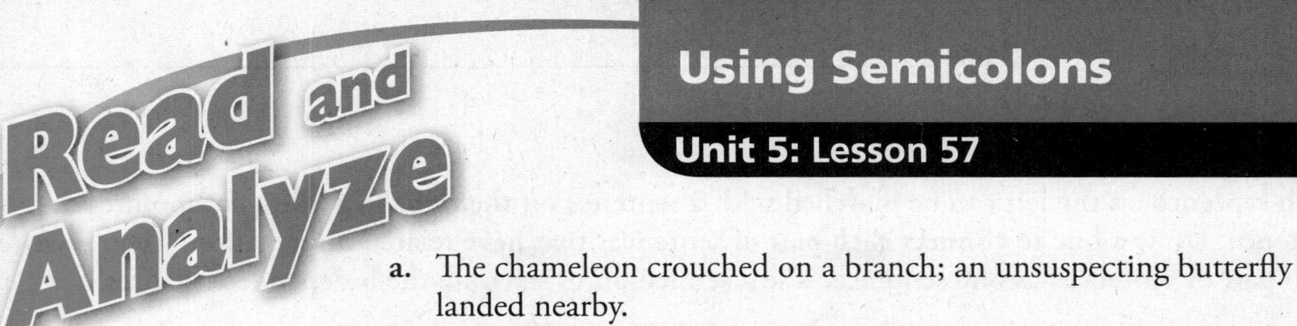

Using Semicolons

Unit 5: Lesson 57

a. The chameleon crouched on a branch; an unsuspecting butterfly landed nearby.
b. Chameleons don't like each other, they must be kept in separate enclosures.

In which sentence do you think the two clauses are separated correctly? ________

A **semicolon** can be used instead of a comma and a conjunction to separate the independent clauses in a compound sentence.

See Handbook Section 8

Practice

Write a semicolon to separate the clauses in each sentence.

1. The chameleon is a very quiet lizard it sits perfectly still.
2. The chameleon's name comes from two Greek words the words mean "dwarf lion."
3. Some chameleons have horns on their heads they use the horns for fighting.
4. Chameleons are adapted for living in trees they can grasp branches with their tails.
5. Chameleons' feet are shaped like hands they have thumbs and fingers.
6. A chameleon's eyes move independently they can focus on two different objects at once.
7. Some chameleons eat insects others eat grasses.
8. Chameleons also change colors a chameleon can make itself gray, black, green, or brown.
9. A chameleon doesn't change color to match its background it can change color as its mood changes.
10. A chameleon that's won a fight for territory might turn bright green the loser might turn gray.
11. Sometimes temperature affects a chameleon's color a chameleon might turn pale when it gets cold.
12. Chameleons aren't the only lizards that change color many lizards have this ability.

A chameleon's powerful tongue can grow as long as its body.

Name ______________________________

Apply

Each sentence on the left can be matched with a sentence on the right to make a compound sentence. Draw a line to connect each pair of sentences that have related information. Then rewrite each pair of sentences as one sentence. Use a semicolon to separate the independent clauses.

Chameleons are usually green or brown.	Insects get trapped on the end of it.
Chameleons move very slowly when hunting.	It can shoot out far and fast.
A chameleon's tongue is long and powerful.	They are hard to see against the leaves.
A chameleon's tongue is also very sticky.	They lift one foot at a time.

13. ______________________________

14. ______________________________

15. ______________________________

16. ______________________________

Reinforce

Use what you have read about chameleons to answer the questions below. Each answer should include two independent clauses separated by a semicolon.

17. What are two interesting features of a chameleon's appearance? ______________________________

18. How does a chameleon move? ______________________________

19. How does a chameleon eat? ______________________________

Read and Analyze

Direct and Indirect Quotations

Unit 5: Lesson 58

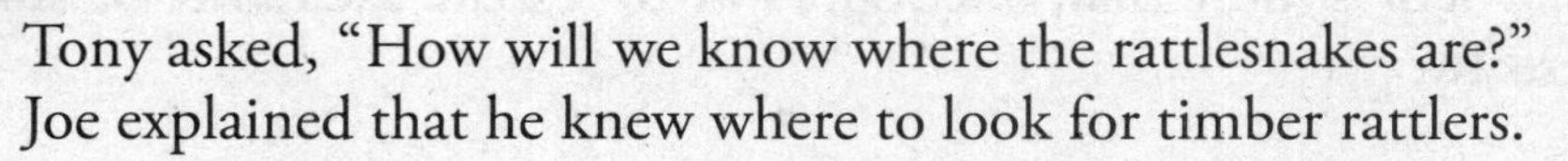

Tony asked, "How will we know where the rattlesnakes are?"
Joe explained that he knew where to look for timber rattlers.

Which sentence shows a speaker's exact words? Underline it.

Circle the marks that begin and end the quotation. Then circle the first letter of the quotation.

A **direct quotation**, or direct speech, is a speaker's exact words. Use **quotation marks** around the beginning and end of a direct quotation. Use a comma to separate the speaker's exact words from the rest of the sentence. Begin a direct quotation with an uppercase letter, and add end punctuation before the last quotation mark. An **indirect quotation** retells a speaker's words. Do not use quotation marks when the words *that* or *whether* come before a speaker's words.

See Handbook Section 4

Practice

Write *I* after each indirect quotation and *D* after each direct quotation. Add quotation marks, commas, and end punctuation to direct quotations. Circle lowercase letters that should be capitalized.

1. Nico asked whether timber rattlesnakes are easy to find. ______
2. They spend more than half the year hibernating in holes and rock cracks Joe said. ______
3. Joe commented that snakes are cold-blooded and need the sun to warm them. ______
4. Timber rattlers warm up on sunny rocks for a few days every spring Joe said. ______
5. That's the best time to see them he added. ______
6. Joe said that rattlesnakes hibernate in groups and return to the same spot each year. ______
7. He said this is an area where I saw snakes sunning themselves last year. ______
8. What's that buzzing sound Tony asked nervously. ______
9. Look! It's a rattlesnake Nico shouted. ______
10. Joe said that we should stay calm and stand back. ______
11. These snakes are poisonous he warned. ______
12. Tony said look at that one's beautiful stripes. ______

Timber rattlesnakes are found in the forests of the eastern United States.

Name ______________________________

Apply

Rewrite each indirect quotation as a direct quotation. Rewrite each direct quotation as an indirect quotation. There is more than one right way to rewrite each one. Be sure to use punctuation marks correctly.

13. "Joe, how does a rattlesnake make its rattling sound?" Nico asked.

____

14. Joe said that a rattlesnake sheds its skin a few times every year.

____

15. "Each time the snake sheds its skin, a loose, hardened piece of skin stays on the end of its tail," Joe explained.

____

____

16. He said that these hardened pieces click together when the snake shakes its tail.

____

Reinforce

Will Joe, Nico, and Tony meet more rattlers? Draw pictures in these boxes to show what will happen to these characters next. Under each box write a direct quotation to tell what a character is saying.

______________________________ ______________________________

______________________________ ______________________________

______________________________ ______________________________

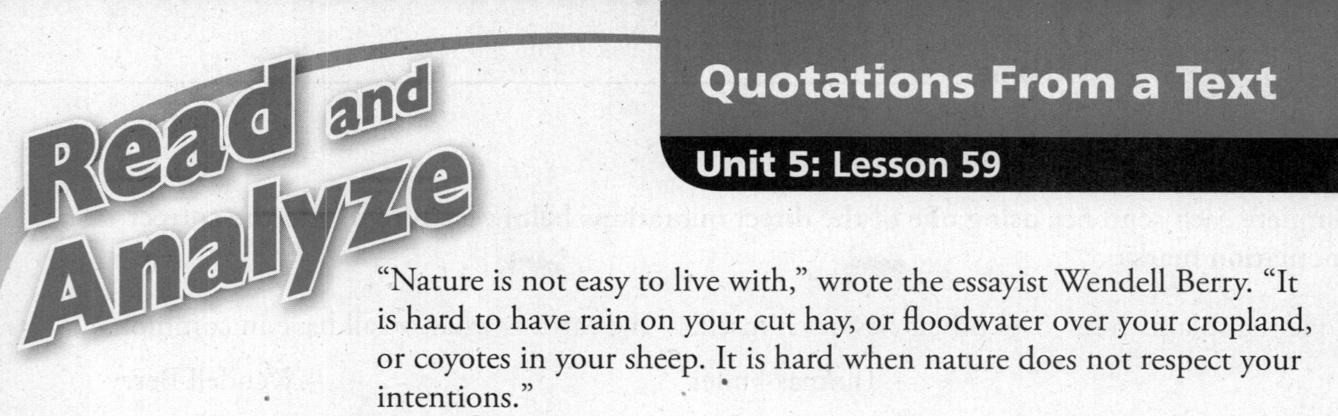

"Nature is not easy to live with," wrote the essayist Wendell Berry. "It is hard to have rain on your cut hay, or floodwater over your cropland, or coyotes in your sheep. It is hard when nature does not respect your intentions."

Circle each punctuation mark that tells the reader that the writer is using a quotation from a text.

You can make a report more interesting and informative by including a **quotation from a text** by an expert on the subject you are writing about. Use **quotation marks** at the beginning and end of a direct quotation. Use a comma to separate the speaker's exact words from the rest of the sentence. Begin a direct quotation with an uppercase letter. Add end punctuation (period, question mark, exclamation point, or comma in place of a period) before the last quotation mark.

See Handbook Sections 4 and 8

Practice

Add quotation marks and commas so that each direct quotation below is written correctly.

1. The ancient Greek poet Theocritus seemingly yearned for a simpler life. He wrote Oh, to be a frog, my lords, and live aloof from care.
2. Marie Curie, winner of Nobel Prizes in physics and chemistry, said All my life through, the new sights of nature made me rejoice like a child.
3. The ancient Greek philosopher and scientist Aristotle was also inspired by the natural world. He wrote In all things of nature there is something of the marvelous.
4. The American poet Robert Frost believed that nature is a great teacher. He wrote How many times it thundered before Franklin took the hint! How many apples fell on Newton's head before he took the hint. Nature is always hinting at us. It hints over and over again. And suddenly we take the hint.
5. The English poet William Wordsworth seems to agree with Frost. Wordsworth wrote Let Nature be your teacher.

Lesson 59 Name ____________________

Apply

Complete each sentence using one of the direct quotations below. Be sure to add the correct punctuation marks.

He that plants trees loves others besides himself.
—Thomas Fuller

The earth is what we all have in common.
—Wendell Berry

When one tugs at a single thing in nature, he finds it attached to the rest of the world.
—John Muir

6. I've always been inspired by Thomas Fuller's quote ____________________

____

7. Wendell Berry was correct when he noted ____________________

____

8. How true is John Muir's quote ____________________

____

Reinforce

Write a short paragraph about a type of animal you believe is important to protect or treat well. Tell why you feel this way. Include a quotation from a text in your paragraph.

____

____

____

____

____

____

____

____

____

____

Read and Analyze

Camp Iguana
Box B-755
Yuma, AZ 85364
August 10, 20__

Dear Miguel,

Today is the hottest day of the year so far! Tomorrow morning we're supposed to go on a nature hike in the Yuma Desert. If tomorrow is as hot as today, I'll bet the hike will be cancelled. Write soon!

Your buddy,
Ron

Circle the commas in the heading of this letter. Underline the comma in the greeting. Draw a box around the comma in the closing.

A **friendly letter** has five parts: the heading, the greeting, the body, the closing, and the signature. In the heading, use a comma between the city and the state abbreviation, and between the date and the year. Capitalize all important words. Use commas also at the end of the greeting and the closing. A **formal e-mail** is similar to a letter, but it usually has only four parts: the greeting, the body, the closing, and the signature.

See Handbook Sections 8, 29, and 30

Practice

Add commas where they are needed in the letter below.

116 Hope St.
Baltimore MD 21210
August 15 20__

Dear Ron

Nestor and I visited the Taylor Natural History Museum this morning. The snake keeper let me hold a humongous boa constrictor. I was very surprised: its body felt cool and dry, not hot and slimy as I had expected.

Did you ever get to take that desert hike? If you did, maybe you have a snake story to tell, too! Well, that's all for now.

Your pal
Miguel

Name

Apply

Rewrite this friendly letter on the lines below. Use correct capitalization and punctuation.

camp livingston 1100 pitcher road ross springs OH 43210 July 10 20__ dear sandra today at camp we caught tadpoles for the aquarium. I'll write to tell you when they grow into frogs. Your friend denise

Reinforce

See Handbook Section 32

Ask an adult to help you use the Internet to research a state or national park you would like to visit. Then write a formal e-mail to the park in which you request information. For example, you might ask whether the park offers tours or what wildlife might be seen at a particular time of year. Write a draft of your email below.

Quotation Marks and Apostrophes

Write *D* after each direct quotation and *I* after each indirect quotation. Add quotation marks and other punctuation marks to direct quotations. Draw three lines ( ) under letters that should be capitalized.

1. Mr. Chi said that we were going to see a movie about how lizards defend themselves. _____
2. Trinh shouted the skink broke off its own tail and got away! _____
3. Mr. Chi told us that this is an unusual kind of defense. _____
4. Biologist Barry Commoner wrote The proper use of science is not to conquer nature but to live with it.
5. The essayist Ralph Waldo Emerson wrote Adopt the pace of nature: her secret is patience.

Underline the correct word in each pair. Write *C* if the answer is a contraction. Write *P* if the answer is a possessive.

6. Many people (can't/cant') tell the difference between salamanders and lizards. _____
7. (Salamanders'/Salamander's) bodies look like the bodies of lizards. _____
8. A (lizards'/lizard's) skin is dry and scaly, but salamanders have moist skin. _____

Commas and Semicolons

Add commas and semicolons where they are needed. Cross out commas that are not needed.

9. "Some of, the largest lizards can be found in Africa India and Australia," said Ms. Kaplan.
10. "Which lizard is the biggest Ms. Kaplan?" Katie asked.
11. "Well the world's largest lizard is, the Komodo dragon," said Ms. Kaplan.
12. These lizards hatch from small eggs but they grow to be over ten feet long.
13. Komodo dragons are very rare they live only on a few islands in Indonesia.
14. The zoo had a special display of Komodo dragons I saw it.
15. I watched Komodo dragons eat walk and sleep.

Unit 5 **Review** Name ________________________________

Punctuation and Capitalization

Use proofreading marks to correct each capitalization or punctuation error. Then label each sentence *declarative, interrogative, imperative,* or *exclamatory.*

16. did you know that some snakes are called "flying snakes." ____________________

17. Look at the snake in this picture? ____________________

18. It can glide through the air for short distances ____________________

19. wow, that's amazing. ____________________

20. Its belly scales act like a parachute? ____________________

Use proofreading marks to correct each capitalization or punctuation error. Add underlines and quotation marks where they are needed.

21. professor starsky said that japanese giant salamanders can grow to be over five feet long.

22. These huge amphibians live only on the island of honshu in japan.

23. mr f b Baker's Enterprise Productions inc is making a movie about giant salamanders.

24. His studio is on Main st near the shoe factory.

25. The movie will be called salamanders are super.

26. It is based on a book titled the japanese giant salamander.

27. The movie's theme song will be dance of the amphibians.

28. I like the poem salamander soup.

29. I just bought a pair of froggy flyers; they are a brand of athletic shoes.

Letters

Rewrite this friendly letter correctly on a separate sheet of paper.

30. Camp Komodo markland NJ 07902 June 22 20__ dear Matt I can't wait for your visit. We're going to have a great time! Wait until you see my pet salamander. I'll see you next week. your friend Daniel

Spelling Practice

Read and Analyze

Liz took a **photograph** of a lizard that was ten **centimeters** long.

Circle the word in bold type that has a Greek root that means "to measure."

Greek and Latin Roots

Many words in English have major parts, or **roots**, that come from the ancient Greek and Roman languages. For example, *telephone*, *photocopy*, *graphics*, and *millimeter* contain the Greek roots *tele* ("distant"), *photo* ("light"), *graph* ("written"), and *meter* ("measure"). *Inspect*, *describe*, *disrupt*, *export*, *eject*, and *dictate* contain the Latin roots spec ("see"), *scrib* ("write"), *rupt* ("break apart"), *port* ("carry"), *ject* ("throw"), and *dict* ("speak").

Word Sort

Use the words below to complete the word sort.

predict	prescribe	telecast	photocopy	thermometer
prospect	reject	erupt	import	photograph

Greek roots (*tele, photo, graph, meter*)	**Latin roots (*spec, scrib, rupt, port, ject, dict*)**

Name ______________________________

Pattern Practice

dictionary	telescope	biography	portable
inspector	photocopy	erupt	

Write the word that answers each question.

1. Which word has a Greek root that means "light"? ______________________
2. Which word has a Latin root that means "break apart"? ______________________
3. Which word has a Latin root that means "speak"? ______________________
4. Which word has a Greek root that means "written"? ______________________
5. Which word has a Latin root that means "see"? ______________________
6. Which word has a Greek root that means "distant"? ______________________
7. Which word has a Latin root that means "carry"? ______________________

Write the word from above that best completes each sentence.

8. You should read this ______________________ about Ben Franklin's life.
9. It is hard to tell when the volcano will ______________________ again.
10. Because the speakers are ______________________, I can take them anywhere.
11. Lily tracks the movement of the stars with her ______________________.
12. Use a ______________________ to check the word's meaning.

Use the **Dictionary**

Write a word that begins with each Greek or Latin root. Use a dictionary to find words and check spellings.

13. photo ______________________
14. spec ______________________
15. tele ______________________

Proofreading Practice

Find the mistakes in the letter below. Use proofreading marks to show how to fix each mistake. Use a dictionary to check and correct spellings.

Proofreading Marks

Mark	Means	Example
∧	add	Iguanas ∧(have) long tails.
≡	make into an uppercase letter	iguanas have long tails.
/	make into a lowercase letter	Iguanas Have long tails.
⊙	add a period	Iguanas have long tails⊙
∧ (with comma)	add a comma	Yes∧ iguanas have long tails.
“ ”	add quotation marks	“Iguanas have long tails,” he said.
(sp)	fix spelling	Igwanas have long tails.
’	add an apostrophe	Iguanas’ tails are long.

224 Hummingbird st
Los Angeles, CA 90012
May 11 2012

dear Max,

Last weekend my dad and I drove into the mojave Desert, I was looking for lizards. I borrowed my moms binoculars. I also brought along a book, the story of reptiles, by dr R L Jackson.

We hiked into a canyon. All of a sudden, Dad shouted “Kevin look there?” A lizard skittered by but I got a good look at it. I found a picture of the lizard in my book, it was a chuckwalla.

Chuckwallas store water in sacs under their skin they are able to survive in temperatures of up to 113° F. The chuckwalla is a species of iguana.

Ive learned some amazing facts about iguanas. Most iguanas eat fruit, leafs, or insecs. One species in South america can run across the Surface of a pool of water without sinking. Another one in Fiji turns from bright green to black when it’s frightened. I wrote a poem called i want to be an iguana.

Would you like to visit next month. we could look for lizards in my yard.

Your friend
Kevin

Name ____________________

Proofreading Checklist

You can use the list below to help you find and fix mistakes in your own writing. Write the titles of your own stories or reports in the blanks on top of the chart. Then use the questions to check your work. Make a check mark (✓) in each box after you have checked that item.

Proofreading Checklist for Unit 5

	Titles			
Have I capitalized proper nouns, proper adjectives, and all the important words in titles?				
Have I placed quotation marks around direct quotations?				
Have I used commas to separate items in a series?				
Have I joined each compound sentence with a comma followed by a conjunction or with a semicolon?				

Also Remember…

Does each sentence begin with an uppercase letter and end with the right end mark?				
Do all abbreviations begin with an uppercase letter and end with a period?				
Did I use a dictionary to check and correct spellings?				
Have I used contractions correctly?				

Your Own List

Use this space to write your own list of things to check in your writing.

School Home Connection

In Unit 5 of *Grammar, Usage, and Mechanics,* students are learning which letters to capitalize and how to use punctuation marks such as periods, apostrophes, commas, and quotation marks. The activities on this page give extra practice with some of the concepts in this unit. You can help your child use the information he or she is learning in school by choosing one or more activities to complete with him or her at home.

Word Search **(Apostrophes)**

Work with your child to find the eleven words hidden in the word search. Then ask your child to write as many contractions as possible by combining these words in different ways.

Example The word *don't* is formed by combining *do* and *not*.

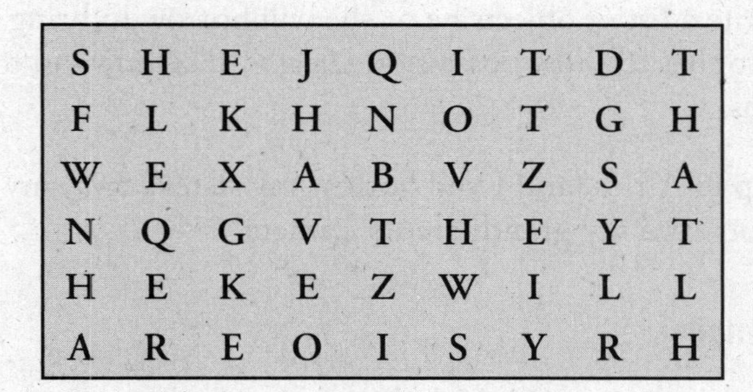

S	H	E	J	Q	I	T	D	T
F	L	K	H	N	O	T	G	H
W	E	X	A	B	V	Z	S	A
N	Q	G	V	T	H	E	Y	T
H	E	K	E	Z	W	I	L	L
A	R	E	O	I	S	Y	R	H

Postcard **(Proper Nouns and Proper Adjectives; Initials and Abbreviations)**

Help your child use a 4" × 6" blank card to design his or her own postcard. First have your child draw a picture on one side of the card. Then have him or her draw a line down the middle of the back of the card and write a message on the left side of the line. Help your child write the address of a friend or family member on the right side. Encourage your child to capitalize proper nouns and use abbreviations (*St., Ave.*).

Thumbs Up/Thumbs Down **(Titles)**

Ask your child to write a short review of a favorite book, movie, or song. Then ask him or her to write a review of a book, movie, or song he or she did not enjoy. Invite your child to be specific about what he or she liked or disliked. Remind your child to capitalize all important words in any title. He or she should underline the titles of books and movies and use quotation marks around titles of songs.

Name ____

The Envelope, Please (Titles)

Ask each member of your family to write the title of a favorite movie, book, and story on a slip of paper. Put all the slips in a hat or bag. Then work with your child to use the slips and create a poster of these favorites. Make sure your child underlines movie titles and book titles and puts quotation marks around story titles. Decorate the poster and give it to another family you know.

Favorite Movie
Ratatouille
Best Book
George Washington's Teeth
Greatest Story
"The Gold Coin"

Traveling Game (Apostrophes; Commas in a Series)

Play a game with your child in which you plan an imaginary trip. Have your child write a list of objects he or she will borrow to bring on the trip. Encourage your child to use apostrophes to show possession (*Lucia's, students'*) and to separate the items in his or her list with commas.

Example I'm going on a trip to Africa, and I will borrow my **sister's** tent, my **teacher's** map, Alex's cowboy boots, and my **grandparents'** camera.

Pen Pal (Friendly Letters and E-mails)

Encourage your child to begin writing to a pen pal. Help him or her find a pen pal through an organization such as KidsCom (www.kidscom.com). If your child uses e-mail to correspond, remind him or her to include a greeting, body, closing, and signature. If your child writes a friendly letter, remind him or her to include all five parts of a letter.

The Show Must Go On! (Commas)

Invite your child to write a very short play. Suggest that he or she use introductory elements (such as *Yes, No,* and *Well*) and direct address (for example, *Carl, come here!*) in the dialogue. Make sure your child uses commas to separate these elements from the rest of a sentence. Then read the play out loud with your child. Point out to him or her the way commas make a reader pause.

Example

SCENE ONE

Ballet Dancer: Ouch, my ankle!

Stage Hand: Hurry, we have to find a doctor!

SCENE TWO

Ballet Dancer: Will I ever dance again, Dr. Woo?

Doctor: Well, you've had a bad sprain, but with some rest you'll be fine.

Appendix Table of Contents

TEST TIP: Read all four answer choices carefully before choosing and marking the answer you think is correct.

Read each item carefully. Fill in the circle next to the best answer.

1. **Read this sentence.**

Farm ponds attract wildlife of many kinds.

   What is the complete subject of this sentence?

   Ⓐ ponds
   Ⓑ farm ponds
   Ⓒ ponds attract
   Ⓓ wildlife

2. **Read this sentence.**

Some farmers make their ponds attractive to wildlife.

   What are the simple subject and simple predicate of this sentence?

   Ⓐ some; farmers
   Ⓑ ponds; attractive
   Ⓒ make; ponds
   Ⓓ farmers; make

3. **Which of the following sentences has a compound predicate?**

   Ⓐ Some farmers build sediment traps and ponds.
   Ⓑ The traps and ponds receive irrigation water.
   Ⓒ Irrigation water carries fertilizer and pesticides.
   Ⓓ The traps absorb the water and remove chemicals.

4. **Read this sentence.**

Farm ponds provide a habitat for frogs.

   What is the direct object in this sentence?

   Ⓐ farm
   Ⓑ provide
   Ⓒ habitat
   Ⓓ frogs

5. **Read this sentence.**

Frogs give farmers <u>help</u> with pest control.

   The direct object in this sentence is underlined. What is the indirect object?

   Ⓐ frogs
   Ⓑ farmers
   Ⓒ pest
   Ⓓ control

6. **Read these sentences.**

Frogs are hungry creatures. Flies are yummy to frogs.

   Which statement tells about the sentences?

   Ⓐ The first sentence contains a predicate noun, and the second contains a predicate adjective.
   Ⓑ The first sentence contains a predicate adjective, and the second contains a predicate noun.
   Ⓒ Both sentences contain predicate nouns.
   Ⓓ Both sentences contain predicate adjectives.

7. **Which sentence has a prepositional phrase underlined?**

   Ⓐ <u>Hawks and owls</u> may hunt near a farm pond.
   Ⓑ An egret <u>or a heron</u> may take up residence.
   Ⓒ Native grasses <u>provide cover</u> for birds.
   Ⓓ Helpful insects can thrive <u>in grassy areas</u>.

Name ______________________________

Read each item carefully. Fill in the circle next to the best answer.

8. Which sentence is a compound sentence?

Ⓐ Flocks of migratory birds stop and rest at farm ponds.
Ⓑ Toads and reptiles make their homes near these ponds.
Ⓒ Birds, frogs, toads, and reptiles can be helpful because they eat insect pests.
Ⓓ Fewer pests mean healthier crops, and healthier crops mean more money for the farmer.

9. Read this sentence.

Although farm ponds take up space, they can make farms more productive.

What is the dependent clause in this sentence?

Ⓐ although farm ponds take up space
Ⓑ farm ponds take up space
Ⓒ they can make farms more productive
Ⓓ make farms more productive

10. Which sentence is a complex sentence?

Ⓐ My aunt and uncle built a different kind of pond on their farm.
Ⓑ They call it a pond, but it is more like a small lake.
Ⓒ Water skiers come from miles around and ski on this pond.
Ⓓ Whenever I visit their farm, I practice my jumps and turns.

11. Read this sentence.

My sister and I enjoy chores that help us learn about farming.

Which word in this sentence is a relative pronoun?

Ⓐ my
Ⓑ I
Ⓒ that
Ⓓ us

12. Read this item.

Students help with some farm pond projects, they plant wild shrubs and grasses.

How should this sentence be rewritten?

Ⓐ Change *Students help* to *Students, they help*.
Ⓑ Insert the word *although* after the comma.
Ⓒ Change the comma to a period, and capitalize the word *they*.
Ⓓ It should not be rewritten. It is written correctly.

13. Read this sentence.

Some giant bluefin tuna live for thirty years.

What is the complete subject of this sentence?

Ⓐ some giant bluefin tuna
Ⓑ bluefin tuna
Ⓒ tuna live
Ⓓ for thirty years

Read each item carefully. Fill in the circle next to the best answer.

14. Read this sentence.

> These huge fish range from Arctic waters to tropical regions.

What are the simple subject and simple predicate of this sentence?

Ⓐ huge; fish
Ⓑ fish; range
Ⓒ range; from
Ⓓ Arctic; waters

15. Which of the following sentences has a compound predicate?

Ⓐ The meat of this fish is prized for its texture and its taste.
Ⓑ Ancient peoples caught bluefin and painted pictures of them on cave walls.
Ⓒ Today fishing crews search for bluefin tuna with high-tech equipment.
Ⓓ Large numbers of bluefin have been caught, and these fish are now rare in many areas.

16. Read this sentence.

> Fishing crews chase bluefin at high speeds.

What is the direct object in this sentence?

Ⓐ crews
Ⓑ chase
Ⓒ bluefin
Ⓓ speeds

17. Read this sentence.

> A large catch of bluefin brings a crew a huge profit.

The direct object in this sentence is underlined. What is the indirect object?

Ⓐ bluefin
Ⓑ brings
Ⓒ crew
Ⓓ huge

18. Read these sentences.

> Bluefin tuna are swift swimmers.
>
> Adults are very large.

Which statement tells about the sentences?

Ⓐ The first sentence contains a predicate noun, and the second contains a predicate adjective.
Ⓑ The first sentence contains a predicate adjective, and the second contains a predicate noun.
Ⓒ Both sentences contain predicate nouns.
Ⓓ Both sentences contain predicate adjectives.

19. Which sentence has a prepositional phrase underlined?

Ⓐ Bluefin tuna are warm-blooded fish.
Ⓑ They live in icy waters and can dive deeply.
Ⓒ These fish once were numerous in the Mediterranean Sea.
Ⓓ Overfishing has greatly reduced the number of bluefin tuna there.

Name ____________________

Read each item carefully. Fill in the circle next to the best answer.

20. Which sentence is a compound sentence?

Ⓐ Bluefin are protected by laws in some areas, but not all fishing crews obey the laws.
Ⓑ Scientists count bluefin populations and study their behavior.
Ⓒ The extinction of this remarkable and valuable fish seems a possibility.
Ⓓ Protection of this species requires international cooperation and greater enforcement of laws.

21. Read this sentence.

> Giant bluefin still flourish near Alaska because that state effectively manages fishing there.

What is the dependent clause in this sentence?

Ⓐ giant bluefin still flourish near Alaska
Ⓑ still flourish near Alaska
Ⓒ that state effectively manages fishing there
Ⓓ because that state effectively manages fishing there

22. Which sentence is a complex sentence?

Ⓐ New Zealand protects its bluefin tuna population, and Iceland does, too.
Ⓑ The establishment of protected areas does not keep bluefin tuna safe, however.
Ⓒ When these fish migrate through unprotected areas, they can be caught.
Ⓓ The United States belongs to tuna protection groups, but these groups have not been effective.

23. Read this sentence.

> Yellowfin tuna that is caught off U.S. shores is an ocean-friendly choice.

Which word in this sentence is a relative pronoun?

Ⓐ that
Ⓑ off
Ⓒ is
Ⓓ choice

24. Read this sentence.

> Another ocean-friendly choice is albacore tuna caught by the troll pole method in waters where these fish are plentiful.

Which word in this sentence is a relative adverb?

Ⓐ is
Ⓑ by
Ⓒ in
Ⓓ where

25. Read this sentence.

> You can find information on the Internet about ocean-friendly fishing, the Monterey Bay Aquarium Seafood Watch is an informative website.

How should this sentence be rewritten?

Ⓐ Insert a comma between *Watch* and *is.*
Ⓑ Make it into two sentences by changing the comma to a period and capitalizing *the.*
Ⓒ Remove the comma between *fishing* and *the.*
Ⓓ Add the word *although* after the comma and before *the.*

TEST TIP: Don't spend too much time on one question.

Read each item carefully. Fill in the circle next to the best answer.

1. Which of the following sentences has a proper noun underlined?

Ⓐ Let me show you this <u>timeline</u>.
Ⓑ It shows the dates of early voyages to our <u>continent</u>.
Ⓒ Not all dates are <u>exact</u>.
Ⓓ No one knows exactly when <u>Leif Ericson</u> sailed to North America.

2. Which of the following sentences has a possessive noun in it?

Ⓐ Christopher Columbus moved to Lisbon, Portugal, at the age of 25.
Ⓑ In that city he learned to read and write.
Ⓒ Christopher Columbus's brother taught him mapmaking skills.
Ⓓ These skills helped him prepare for his historic voyage.

3. Read this sentence.

In the colonial period, some settlers built cabins out of whole logs.

Which of these nouns is an abstract noun?

Ⓐ period
Ⓑ settlers
Ⓒ cabins
Ⓓ logs

4. Read this sentence.

Many New England colonists built their homes out of logs.

Which word in the sentence is a possessive pronoun?

Ⓐ many
Ⓑ New England
Ⓒ their
Ⓓ of

5. Which of the following sentences has a linking verb in boldfaced type?

Ⓐ Sara **collects** commemorative American stamps.
Ⓑ This stamp **depicts** the first flight by the Wright Brothers.
Ⓒ I **like** stamps with scenes from the American Revolution.
Ⓓ This stamp **is** the oldest one in my collection.

6. Read this sentence.

Our family has visited Paul Revere's house in Boston, Massachusetts.

What is the main verb in this sentence?

Ⓐ family
Ⓑ has
Ⓒ visited
Ⓓ house

7. Read this sentence.

Yes, you **may** borrow my American history book this weekend.

What is the special function of the modal auxiliary in boldfaced type?

Ⓐ to indicate ability
Ⓑ to communicate an obligation
Ⓒ to indicate possibility
Ⓓ to give permission

 Name ________________

Read each item carefully. Fill in the circle next to the best answer.

8. Read this sentence.

Travelers in colonial America generally depended on horses for transportation.

Which of these words is an adjective in the sentence?

Ⓐ colonial
Ⓑ generally
Ⓒ depended
Ⓓ for

9. Read this sentence.

On a trip from Boston to New York in 1704, Sarah Knight narrowly avoided a tragic fall into a river.

Which of these words is an adverb in the sentence?

Ⓐ from
Ⓑ 1704
Ⓒ narrowly
Ⓓ tragic

10. Read this sentence.

We live in a large rectangular state famous for its blue clear skies.

How should this sentence be rewritten?

Ⓐ Change *large rectangular* to *rectangular large*.
Ⓑ Change *blue clear* to *clear blue*.
Ⓒ Change *large rectangular* to *rectangular large* and *blue clear* to *clear blue*.
Ⓓ Make no change. The sentence is correct as written.

11. **Which of the following sentences has a subordinating conjunction in it?**

Ⓐ Benjamin Franklin traveled to Philadelphia at age 17.
Ⓑ He worked as a printer, but he also invented devices.
Ⓒ One of his inventions was the lightning rod.
Ⓓ Before he invented this device, lightning caused many house fires.

12. **Which sentence has a pair of correlative conjunctions?**

Ⓐ Most roads in the American colonies were just dirt paths.
Ⓑ These roads were either muddy or dusty most of the year.
Ⓒ Rocks littered main roads, and fallen trees sometimes blocked them.
Ⓓ Steep hills caused problems for horses with heavily loaded wagons.

13. **Which of the following sentences has a proper noun underlined?**

Ⓐ Where can we go to see totem <u>poles</u>?
Ⓑ The Indians of the <u>Northwest Coast</u> carved them.
Ⓒ That totem pole commemorates an important <u>event</u> in a person's life.
Ⓓ A few Northwest Indian <u>artists</u> still carve these poles today.

Read each item carefully. Fill in the circle next to the best answer.

14. Which of the following sentences has a possessive noun in it?

Ⓐ We are studying America's mountain ranges.
Ⓑ Mountain ranges are barriers to travel.
Ⓒ Daniel Boone led settlers across the Appalachian Mountains.
Ⓓ Lewis and Clark had difficulty crossing the Rockies.

15. Read this sentence.

> No driver of a stagecoach could handle a team of horses as skillfully as Charlie Parkhurst.

Which of these nouns is a collective noun?

Ⓐ driver
Ⓑ stagecoach
Ⓒ team
Ⓓ horses

16. Read this sentence.

> Charlie Parkhurst was the only female driver of stagecoaches at a time when women were excluded from that profession because of discrimination.

Which of these nouns is a concrete noun?

Ⓐ driver
Ⓑ time
Ⓒ profession
Ⓓ discrimination

17. Read this sentence.

> I need to borrow this atlas to use its relief maps.

Which word in the sentence is a possessive pronoun?

Ⓐ this
Ⓑ use
Ⓒ its
Ⓓ relief

18. Which of the following sentences has an action verb in boldfaced type?

Ⓐ Mount Vernon **was** the home of America's first president, George Washington.
Ⓑ The main house **is** 2½ stories high.
Ⓒ Washington and his wife Martha **lived** in this mansion prior to the Revolutionary War.
Ⓓ Mount Vernon **became** home for the Washingtons again after George's second term as president.

19. Read this sentence.

> Before this week I had never seen a bison.

What is the helping verb in this sentence?

Ⓐ before
Ⓑ had
Ⓒ never
Ⓓ seen

Name ______________________________

Read each item carefully. Fill in the circle next to the best answer.

20. Read this sentence.

We **might** have time for a visit to the Lincoln Memorial.

What is the special function of the modal auxiliary in boldfaced type?

Ⓐ to indicate ability
Ⓑ to communicate an obligation
Ⓒ to indicate possibility
Ⓓ to give permission

21. Read this sentence.

Thanks to its fine harbor, Charleston, South Carolina, is an important city.

Which of these words is an adjective in the sentence?

Ⓐ thanks
Ⓑ fine
Ⓒ South Carolina
Ⓓ city

22. Read this sentence.

Ships could dock safely and be protected from stormy seas.

Which of these words is an adverb in the sentence?

Ⓐ could
Ⓑ dock
Ⓒ safely
Ⓓ stormy

23. Read this sentence.

The American first flag had thirteen white stars on a field of blue.

How should this sentence be rewritten?

Ⓐ Change *American first* to *first American*.
Ⓑ Change *thirteen white* to *white thirteen*.
Ⓒ Change *American first* to *first American* and *thirteen white* to *white thirteen*.
Ⓓ Make no change. The sentence is correct as written.

24. Which of the following sentences has a subordinating conjunction in it?

Ⓐ Ships carried rice from Charleston to distant ports.
Ⓑ Rice planters in the Charleston area became prosperous.
Ⓒ Field workers suffered, though; the work was hard and unhealthy.
Ⓓ Because these workers were enslaved people, they could not leave their jobs.

25. Which sentence has a pair of correlative conjunctions?

Ⓐ My grandfather and grandmother came to the United States sixty years ago.
Ⓑ Although they could barely speak English, they opened a small shop.
Ⓒ Not only did they learn English, they also became fluent in Spanish.
Ⓓ They learned Spanish because many of their customers were Spanish speakers.

TEST TIP: Eliminate answer choices that you know are incorrect.

Read each item carefully. Fill in the circle next to the best answer.

1. Read this sentence.

Those athletes want to avoid injury, so ___ warming up carefully.

Which word would complete the sentence correctly?

Ⓐ their
Ⓑ there
Ⓒ they're
Ⓓ theyre

2. Which of the following sentences has *its* or *it's* used *incorrectly*?

Ⓐ It's important to stretch your muscles before competing.
Ⓑ I am going to the gym to use it's exercise machines.
Ⓒ The gym has its schedule posted on the door.
Ⓓ I think it's fun to try new machines.

3. Which of the following sentences has *your* or *you're* used *incorrectly*?

Ⓐ Do you like you're gymnastics coach?
Ⓑ I am amazed at your improvement!
Ⓒ You're the best of anyone on the balance beam.
Ⓓ Perhaps you have improved because you're a hard worker.

4. Read this sentence.

These drills will help me become a ___ soccer player.

Which choice would complete the sentence correctly?

Ⓐ more good
Ⓑ gooder
Ⓒ more better
Ⓓ better

5. Read this sentence.

The fishing rod ___ I use is old but effective.

Which word would complete the sentence correctly?

Ⓐ that
Ⓑ which
Ⓒ who
Ⓓ None of the above

6. Read each sentence. Look at the underlined word in it. Which sentence is written *incorrectly*?

Ⓐ We cannot play with a <u>real</u> baseball here.
Ⓑ We would be <u>very</u> likely to break a window.
Ⓒ This hollow plastic ball is <u>very</u> safe.
Ⓓ It's <u>real</u> good for backyard ball games.

7. Read each sentence. Look at the underlined word in it. Which sentence is written *incorrectly*?

Ⓐ Please <u>set</u> your bag on the floor.
Ⓑ <u>Sit</u> on the bench while I explain the rules.
Ⓒ My sister has <u>sat</u> the paddles on the table.
Ⓓ We have <u>sat</u> long enough; let's play!

Name ______________________________

Read each item carefully. Fill in the circle next to the best answer.

8. **Read this sentence.**

Saleem has ___ a lot about sports from his older brother.

Which word would complete the sentence correctly?

(A) learn
(B) teach
(C) learned
(D) taught

9. **Which of these sentences has *two, to,* or *too* used *incorrectly*?**

(A) This canoe is made for two people.
(B) If one person paddles too hard, the canoe will not travel in a straight line.
(C) My sister and I paddled our canoe from the dock to the opposite shore of the lake.
(D) I love canoeing, and she does, to.

10. **Read each sentence. Look at the underlined word in it. Which sentence is written *incorrectly*?**

(A) My aunt is known throughout the world as a champion.
(B) Her fame grown when she won a race last year.
(C) Few people knew how hard she had trained.
(D) She has grown stronger through exercise.

11. **Read each sentence. Look at the underlined word. Which sentence is written *incorrectly*?**

(A) My uncle bought hisself a fishing boat.
(B) Everyone in our family likes to fish.
(C) There is nothing more relaxing than fishing for striped bass.
(D) I bought myself a fishing rod last month.

12. **Read these sentences.**

My uncle invited my sister and me on a fishing trip. He put ___ boat on a trailer and towed it to Pyramid Lake.

Which pronoun should be used in the second sentence to refer to the boldfaced phrase?

(A) him
(B) his
(C) our
(D) their

13. **Read this sentence.**

Many pitchers do exercises to strengthen ___ legs.

Which word would complete the sentence correctly?

(A) their
(B) there
(C) they're
(D) theyre

Read each item carefully. Fill in the circle next to the best answer.

14. Which of the following sentences has *its* or *it's* used *incorrectly*?

Ⓐ This city is proud of its athletic fields.
Ⓑ It's important for students to get exercise.
Ⓒ Our school opens it's fields to the public.
Ⓓ They are filled with people, except when it's raining.

15. Which of the following sentences has *your* or *you're* used *incorrectly*?

Ⓐ What is your favorite sport?
Ⓑ You're lucky to live near a soccer field.
Ⓒ How often do you play there with your friends?
Ⓓ Call me the next time your going to play there.

16. Read this sentence.

Our team has played hard, but we have the ___ record of all.

Which choice would complete the sentence correctly?

Ⓐ worse
Ⓑ baddest
Ⓒ most bad
Ⓓ worst

17. Read this sentence.

Myra is the batter ___ hit the home run.

Which word would complete the sentence correctly?

Ⓐ that
Ⓑ which
Ⓒ who
Ⓓ None of the above

18. Read each sentence. Look at the underlined word in it. Which sentence is written *incorrectly*?

Ⓐ Is this a <u>real</u> golf club?
Ⓑ It isn't <u>very</u> heavy, and it's quite short.
Ⓒ It's for a young golfer; kids need <u>real</u> equipment to develop skills.
Ⓓ I will pay <u>real</u> careful attention to the instructor.

19. Read each sentence. Look at the underlined word in it. Which sentence is written *incorrectly*?

Ⓐ I <u>sat</u> near mid-court at the basketball game.
Ⓑ I carelessly <u>sat</u> my sunglasses on the bench.
Ⓒ When Cici <u>sat</u> next to me, she broke them.
Ⓓ I should have <u>set</u> those glasses on my locker shelf.

Name ______________________________

Read each item carefully. Fill in the circle next to the best answer.

20. Read this sentence.

Yesterday the coach ___ me how to run hurdles.

Which word would complete the sentence correctly?

Ⓐ learn
Ⓑ teach
Ⓒ learned
Ⓓ taught

21. Which of these sentences has *two, to,* or *too* used *incorrectly*?

Ⓐ I leaped too soon and hit the first hurdle.
Ⓑ I returned to the starting line and tried again.
Ⓒ I leaped over the first to hurdles.
Ⓓ I thought I would clear the third one, too, but I knocked it over.

22. Which of these sentences has *two, to,* or *too* used *incorrectly*?

Ⓐ Each athlete may enter two events.
Ⓑ I will enter the high hurdles and compete in the long jump, too.
Ⓒ In a few minutes I will go too the starting line.
Ⓓ A blue ribbon will be given to the winner of each event.

23. Read each sentence. Look at the underlined word in it. Which sentence is written *incorrectly*?

Ⓐ The home crowd growed quiet.
Ⓑ They knew that the next free throw could decide the game.
Ⓒ The star player swished the shot, and the home team's lead grew.
Ⓓ The fans all said they had known she'd make that free throw.

24. Read each sentence. Look at the underlined word or words. Which sentence is written *incorrectly*?

Ⓐ Lakshmi wrote herself a note.
Ⓑ She did not want anything to go wrong.
Ⓒ With her mom's help, she had packed every thing needed for the hike.
Ⓓ She wanted to be sure her guests would enjoy themselves.

25. Read these sentences.

Lakshmi took out **the trail map**. She unfolded ___ and studied the trail she had chosen for the day's hike.

Which pronoun should be used in the second sentence to refer to the boldfaced phrase?

Ⓐ them
Ⓑ her
Ⓒ its
Ⓓ it

TEST TIP: Be sure to fill in the whole circle on the answer sheet.

Read each item carefully. Fill in the circle next to the best answer.

1. Read this sentence.

When my dad saw me in the stands, he waved.

Which word in the sentence is an object pronoun?

- Ⓐ my
- Ⓑ dad
- Ⓒ me
- Ⓓ he

2. Read each sentence. Look at the underlined word. Which sentence is written *incorrectly*?

- Ⓐ My dad takes my sister and <u>I</u> to the racetrack.
- Ⓑ <u>He</u> and my uncle are part of a pit crew.
- Ⓒ My sister and <u>I</u> are learning about auto mechanics.
- Ⓓ You may see <u>her</u> or me in a pit crew someday.

3. Read each sentence. Look at the underlined verb. Which sentence is *not* correct?

- Ⓐ Drivers on a track always <u>have</u> smooth pavement ahead.
- Ⓑ An off-road race for trucks <u>test</u> the drivers' reflexes.
- Ⓒ Only durable vehicles <u>enter</u> this type of race.
- Ⓓ A long race on dirt roads <u>punishes</u> vehicles and drivers.

4. Read each sentence. Look at the underlined verb. Which sentence is *not* correct?

- Ⓐ That screeching noise <u>is</u> a warning.
- Ⓑ Your car's brake pads <u>are</u> ready for replacement.
- Ⓒ The mechanics in this shop <u>are</u> skillful.
- Ⓓ Repairs on an auto <u>is</u> never cheap.

5. Read this sentence.

My mom ___ our old car last Saturday.

Which verb would complete the sentence correctly?

- Ⓐ sells
- Ⓑ will sell
- Ⓒ sold
- Ⓓ has sold

6. Read this sentence.

By this coming Friday Monica ___ her new midget racer.

Which verb would complete the sentence correctly?

- Ⓐ was piloting
- Ⓑ is piloting
- Ⓒ are piloting
- Ⓓ will be piloting

7. Read this sentence.

So far she _____ only go-karts.

Which verb would complete the sentence correctly?

- Ⓐ had driven
- Ⓑ has driven
- Ⓒ have driven
- Ⓓ will have driven

Name ______________________________

Read each item carefully. Fill in the circle next to the best answer.

8. Read this sentence.

By next Tuesday evening the trucking company ___ her midget racer.

Which verb would complete the sentence correctly?

Ⓐ had delivered
Ⓑ has delivered
Ⓒ have delivered
Ⓓ will have delivered

9. Read this sentence.

Today's resourceful teenagers find several ways to earn money, and they have saved most of the money they earn.

How should this sentence be changed to make it correct?

Ⓐ The verb *find* should be changed to *will find.*
Ⓑ The verb *have saved* should be changed to *save.*
Ⓒ The verb *have saved* should be changed to *saved.*
Ⓓ No change should be made. The sentence is correct as written.

10. Read each sentence. Which sentence has too many negatives?

Ⓐ There isn't no room for any more decals on that car!
Ⓑ I don't think it's possible to count all the decals.
Ⓒ No one knows what that decal stands for.
Ⓓ I would never drive a car covered with ads!

11. Read this sentence.

My model racecar is ___ than my cousin's new model racecar.

Which choice would complete the sentence correctly?

Ⓐ beautifuler
Ⓑ more beautiful
Ⓒ beautifulest
Ⓓ most beautiful

12. Read this sentence.

This car uses fuel the ___ of any car I've tested.

Which choice would complete the sentence correctly?

Ⓐ more efficient
Ⓑ more efficiently
Ⓒ most efficient
Ⓓ most efficiently

13. Read this sentence.

My brother and I bring our car magazines with us on vacation.

Which word in the sentence is an object pronoun?

Ⓐ I
Ⓑ our
Ⓒ magazines
Ⓓ us

Read each item carefully. Fill in the circle next to the best answer.

14. Read each sentence. Look at the underlined word. Which sentence is written *incorrectly*?

Ⓐ Tara and I went to a drag race with her parents.
Ⓑ The noise didn't bother Tara or I.
Ⓒ Tara shared her snack with her parents and me.
Ⓓ She and her parents knew which cars would be the fastest.

15. Read each sentence. Look at the underlined verb. Which sentence is *not* correct?

Ⓐ Drivers in this class learn racing techniques.
Ⓑ The instructor demonstrates the correct position for hands on the steering wheel.
Ⓒ The eyes of a racecar driver looks ahead, to the sides, and in the mirrors.
Ⓓ Any race with other cars requires concentration on the part of the driver.

16. Read each sentence. Look at the underlined verb. Which sentence is *not* correct?

Ⓐ A slick tire is unsafe in wet weather.
Ⓑ An inspection of your tires are a good idea.
Ⓒ Two tires on my car were bald.
Ⓓ Fortunately, a tire sale was in progress.

17. Read this sentence.

> In the future, Brian ___ better care of his car.

Which verb would complete the sentence correctly?

Ⓐ will take
Ⓑ takes
Ⓒ took
Ⓓ has taken

18. Read this sentence.

> Right now sunlight ___ on the track, but soon dark clouds will darken the sky.

Which verb would complete the sentence correctly?

Ⓐ shines
Ⓑ shine
Ⓒ shone
Ⓓ will shine

19. Read this sentence.

> Grandpa ___ a tire when we arrived.

Which verb would complete the sentence correctly?

Ⓐ is changing
Ⓑ are changing
Ⓒ was changing
Ⓓ will be changing

Name ______________________________

Read each item carefully. Fill in the circle next to the best answer.

20. Read this sentence.

Aunt Jill ______ an electric car because she wants to reduce her carbon footprint.

Which verb would complete the sentence correctly?

Ⓐ had bought
Ⓑ has bought
Ⓒ have bought
Ⓓ will have bought

21. Read this sentence.

Before yesterday I never ______ in an electric car.

Which verb would complete the sentence correctly?

Ⓐ had ridden
Ⓑ has ridden
Ⓒ have ridden
Ⓓ will have ridden

22. Read this sentence.

Jill read an article about carbon dioxide in the atmosphere, and she decides to buy a zero-emission vehicle.

How should this sentence be changed to make it correct?

Ⓐ The verb *read* should be changed to *reads*.
Ⓑ The verb *decides* should be changed to *decide*.
Ⓒ The verb *decides* should be changed to *decided*.
Ⓓ No change should be made. The sentence is correct as written.

23. Read each sentence. Which sentence has too many negatives?

Ⓐ I haven't never ridden in such a big car!
Ⓑ I don't think it will fit in our garage.
Ⓒ It isn't easy to drive a big car on a narrow road.
Ⓓ Nobody in our neighborhood owns a car this size.

24. Read this sentence.

Enrique's soap box racer has the ______ time of all, but he is still proud of it.

Which choice would complete the sentence correctly?

Ⓐ slower
Ⓑ more slow
Ⓒ slowest
Ⓓ most slow

25. Read this sentence.

Clete drives ______ now than he did last year.

Which choice would complete the sentence correctly?

Ⓐ more careful
Ⓑ more carefully
Ⓒ most careful
Ⓓ most carefully

TEST TIP: Mark your answers neatly. If you erase, erase completely and clearly without smudging.

Read each item carefully. Fill in the circle next to the best answer.

1. Read this sentence.

What is the largest amphibian alive today!

How should the sentence be changed to make it correct?

Ⓐ Change the exclamation point to a period.
Ⓑ Change the exclamation point to a question mark.
Ⓒ Make the first letter in amphibian an uppercase letter.
Ⓓ Make no change. It is correct as written.

2. Read this sentence.

The <u>japanese</u> <u>salamander</u> is the largest <u>amphibian</u> on our <u>planet</u>.

Which underlined word should be capitalized?

Ⓐ japanese
Ⓑ salamander
Ⓒ amphibian
Ⓓ planet

3. Read this sentence.

<u>Mister Niles Eugene Klein</u> teaches us biology.

How should the underlined name be written with abbreviations?

Ⓐ Mr N E Klein
Ⓑ Mstr. n. e. Klein
Ⓒ Mr. N.E. Klein
Ⓓ Mstr. N.E. Klein

4. Read this sentence.

Soraya borrowed a pair of tough toads, a brand of rain boots, on labor day.

How should the sentence be changed to make it correct?

Ⓐ Make the first letters in *rain, boots, labor,* and *day* uppercase letters.
Ⓑ Make the first letters in *pair, tough, toads, rain,* and *boots* uppercase letters.
Ⓒ Make the first letters in *tough, toads, labor,* and *day* uppercase letters.
Ⓓ Make no change. The sentence is correct as written.

5. Read each sentence. Which sentence has the title in it written correctly?

Ⓐ The book "Prehistoric Amphibians and Their Ancestors" is amazing.
Ⓑ Have you read the short story called *Don't Pet That Frog*?
Ⓒ I just saw the movie "Revenge of the Reptiles."
Ⓓ I am looking for the article titled "Stay Safe Around Snakes."

6. Read each sentence. Look at the underlined word. Which sentence is written *incorrectly*?

Ⓐ One local <u>park's</u> ponds are filled with frogs.
Ⓑ Those <u>frog's</u> croaks are loud and deep.
Ⓒ Frogs are many <u>birds'</u> favorite food.
Ⓓ Some snakes feed on that <u>park's</u> frogs.

Name ______________________________

Read each item carefully. Fill in the circle next to the best answer.

7. Read each sentence. Look at the commas. Which sentence is written correctly?

- Ⓐ Snakes live on the ground, in trees, and in caves.
- Ⓑ Whiptales, racers, and whipsnakes, are fast-moving reptiles.
- Ⓒ Alligators.crocodiles, and caimans are large, dangerous reptiles.
- Ⓓ Snakes have distinctive eyes, tongues, and, tails.

8. Read this sentence.

> "Would you like to be a reptile watcher Sandra?" asked Mr. Tran.

Where should a comma be placed in this sentence?

- Ⓐ after *you*
- Ⓑ after *be*
- Ⓒ after *reptile*
- Ⓓ after *watcher*

9. Read this sentence.

> He told her to bring a notebook and a pencil he warned her to keep a safe distance from any snake she observed.

Where should a semicolon be placed in this sentence?

- Ⓐ after *notebook*
- Ⓑ after *pencil*
- Ⓒ after *distance*
- Ⓓ after *snake*

10. Read each sentence. Which sentence needs to have quotation marks added to it?

- Ⓐ Ariel said that she saw an Eastern hognose snake yesterday.
- Ⓑ Rich asked her what the snake did when it noticed her.
- Ⓒ It hissed and puffed itself up, Ariel replied.
- Ⓓ She said that the snake then flipped on its back and stuck out its tongue.

11. Read this sentence.

> The great explorer and conservationist John Muir wrote "When one tugs at a single thing in nature, he finds it attached to the rest of the world."

What should be done to make this sentence correct?

- Ⓐ Place a comma between *explorer* and *and*.
- Ⓑ Place a comma between *Muir* and *wrote*.
- Ⓒ Place a comma between *wrote* and the first quotation mark.
- Ⓓ Nothing should be done. The sentence is correct as written.

12. Read this friendly letter.

> Dear Amy
>
> Did you borrow my reptile book? If so, please return it. I need it for the nature hike next weekend.
>
> Your friend,
>
> Louis

Where should a comma be placed to make this letter correct?

- Ⓐ after *Amy* in the greeting
- Ⓑ after *borrow* in the body
- Ⓒ after *your* in the closing
- Ⓓ All of the above

Read each item carefully. Fill in the circle next to the best answer.

13. Read this sentence.

> do most amphibians live in moist habitats?

How should the sentence be changed to make it correct?

Ⓐ Change the question mark to an exclamation point.
Ⓑ Change the question mark to a period.
Ⓒ Make the first letter into an uppercase letter.
Ⓓ Make no change. It is correct as written.

14. Read this sentence.

> Central america, a warm, humid area, is home to many species of salamanders.

Which underlined word should be capitalized?

Ⓐ america
Ⓑ area
Ⓒ species
Ⓓ salamanders

15. Read this sentence.

> I asked Professor Jamal Lester Darby about caecilians.

How should the underlined name be written with abbreviations?

Ⓐ Pro. J L Darby
Ⓑ Prof. JL. Darby
Ⓒ Pro JL Darby
Ⓓ Prof. J.L. Darby

16. Read this sentence.

> The cool puddle company of portland, maine, produces rubber sandals called frog clogs.

How should the sentence be changed to make it correct?

Ⓐ Make the first letters in *cool, puddle,* and *company* uppercase letters.
Ⓑ Make the first letters in *cool, puddle, company, portland,* and *maine* uppercase letters.
Ⓒ Make the first letters in *cool, puddle, company, portland, maine, frog,* and *clogs* uppercase letters.
Ⓓ Make no change. The sentence is correct as written.

17. Read each sentence. Which sentence has the title in it written correctly?

Ⓐ Larkin taught us the song The Toad on the Road.
Ⓑ The movie titled Jungle Squeeze is about boa constrictors.
Ⓒ "How to Raise Frogs" is a book I will not read.
Ⓓ My poem Turtle Journey is the best one I've written.

18. Read each sentence. Look at the underlined word. Which sentence is written *incorrectly*?

Ⓐ An amphibian's skin has no scales.
Ⓑ This newt's skin is smooth.
Ⓒ Those amphibians' glands produce mucus, which covers the skin.
Ⓓ That toads' skin feels like leather.

Name ______________________________

Read each item carefully. Fill in the circle next to the best answer.

19. Read each sentence. Look at the commas. Which sentence is written correctly?

Ⓐ Snakes, lizards, and iguanas, are reptiles.
Ⓑ Eastern fence lizards can be seen on rocks, fences, and, trees.
Ⓒ Many lizards eat tadpoles frogs and small fish.
Ⓓ Female iguanas have brown, white, and black markings.

20. Read this sentence.

> "Oh every lizard has legs," said Stephanie.

Where should a comma be placed in this sentence?

Ⓐ after *Oh*
Ⓑ after *every*
Ⓒ after *lizard*
Ⓓ after *said*

21. Read this sentence.

> "Although it looks like a snake the glass lizard is a lizard that does not have legs," the ranger said to us.

Where should a comma be placed in this sentence?

Ⓐ after *Although*
Ⓑ between *lizard* and *is*
Ⓒ after *snake*
Ⓓ after *said*

22. Read this sentence.

> Spectacled caimans now live in southern Florida scientists believe they were brought from South America and released.

Where should a semicolon be placed in this sentence?

Ⓐ after *caimans*
Ⓑ after *Florida*
Ⓒ after *brought*
Ⓓ after *America*

23. Read each sentence. Which sentence needs to have quotation marks added to it?

Ⓐ Ron asked Kesh to tell him which reptile has the longest tail.
Ⓑ Kesh said that the saltwater crocodile is the reptile with the longest tail.
Ⓒ He explained that a large saltwater crocodile's tail can be 13 feet long.
Ⓓ Ron said, I wonder how big its jaws are.

24. Read this quotation from a text:

> Lorraine Anderson expressed her appreciation of nature by writing, Nature has been, for me, for as long as I remember, a source of solace, inspiration, adventure, and delight; a home, a teacher, a companion.

Where should quotation marks be placed to make this correct?

Ⓐ before *Lorraine* and after *companion*
Ⓑ before *expressed* and after *companion*
Ⓒ before *Nature* and after *companion*
Ⓓ No quotation marks are needed. The quotation is correct as written.

25. Read this friendly letter.

> Dear Mrs. Elliot,
>
> I understand that you have a pet iguana. Would it be possible for me to come over and observe it? I am doing a report on that reptile for school.
>
> Sincerely
> David Jefferson

In which part of the letter is a comma missing?

Ⓐ the greeting
Ⓑ the body
Ⓒ the closing
Ⓓ It is correct as written.

Lesson 1 **Underline the complete subject in each sentence once. Underline the complete predicate twice.**

1. Hot sand covered Zoe's feet.
2. She rested beside a pile of driftwood.
3. This hidden beach was her favorite place.
4. Zoe fell asleep.
5. A noisy sea gull landed at her feet.
6. Someone's radio blasted loud music.
7. Some teenagers set up a volleyball net.
8. A crowd gathered.
9. Everyone cheered the players.
10. A quiet place is hard to find.

Lesson 2 **In each sentence, draw one line under the simple subject and two lines under the simple predicate.**

1. My alarm rang at 6:30 this morning.
2. I looked out the window.
3. Heavy black clouds threatened rain.
4. I dressed in warm clothes.
5. My father prepared a hot breakfast for everyone.
6. My mother packed an umbrella in my backpack.
7. A crowd waited impatiently for the bus.
8. The first raindrops were huge.
9. My umbrella snapped in the wind.
10. Randy shared his umbrella with me.

Extra Practice

Name ______________________________

Lesson 3 · **Each sentence below has either a compound subject or a compound predicate. Write *S* next to each sentence with a compound subject. Circle the two subjects. Write *P* next to each sentence with a compound predicate. Underline the two verbs.**

1. The travelers stopped at the edge of the plateau and looked across the desert plain. _____
2. Grasses and shrubs grew in clumps. _____
3. The travelers saw a small oasis and headed in that direction. _____
4. A salamander and a lizard slithered across their path. _____
5. The lizard crawled onto a rock and sat warming itself in the sun. _____
6. The boy and his father smiled at each other. _____
7. The boy grabbed at the lizard and missed. _____
8. Trees and green grasses grow in an oasis. _____
9. The travelers stopped at the oasis and rested for a while. _____
10. The fresh water and cool shade attract many travelers. _____

Lesson 4 **Circle the direct object in each sentence below.**

1. The diver stretched her muscles.
2. The announcer called her name.
3. Her parents watched their daughter anxiously.
4. She quickly climbed the ladder.
5. She focused her concentration.
6. She executed the dive perfectly.
7. She entered the water smoothly.
8. The announcer called out a perfect score.
9. The diver's fans clapped their hands.
10. The girl hugged her parents.

Lesson 5 **The direct object in each sentence is printed in bold type. Circle the indirect object in each sentence.**

1. Bif sent his cousin a **bag** of marbles.
2. His cousin sent Bif a thank you **note**.
3. She also sent Bif an **invitation** to her birthday party.
4. Bif's father gave him **permission** to drive to the party.
5. He mailed his cousin a **postcard** saying he could come.
6. Bif's mother handed him the **keys** to the car.
7. He gave his family one last **wave** and headed for Spokane.
8. He handed the toll taker a five dollar **bill** and waited for change.
9. When Bif arrived, his cousin gave him a big **hug**.
10. At the party Bif sang his cousin a special birthday **song** he wrote for her.

Lesson 6 **Draw a box around the linking verb in each sentence. Then circle each boldfaced word that is a predicate noun. Underline each boldfaced word that is a predicate adjective.**

1. Martin Luther King Jr. was an important **leader** of the civil rights movement in the United States.
2. He was a Baptist **minister.**
3. He was the **leader** of a bus boycott in Montgomery, Alabama, in 1955–1956.
4. Dr. King's demonstrations were **nonviolent**.
5. Some Montgomery residents were **angry** about segregation.
6. The boycott was **successful** in ending segregated seating on public buses.
7. Dr. King was an eloquent **speaker.**
8. His "I Have a Dream" speech is still an **inspiration.**
9. Dr. King's assassination in 1968 was **tragic.**
10. People across the United States were **upset** by his death.

Name ______________________________

Lesson 7 **Underline the prepositional phrase in each sentence. Circle the preposition that begins the prepositional phrase.**

1. It had rained for 11 days.
2. Water gushed into creeks and streams.
3. We went to the river's edge.
4. The river carried huge logs in its current.
5. Many river residents spent the night in hotels.
6. We listened to the radio report.
7. The flood waters crested at midnight.
8. The next day, many people returned to their homes.
9. Our house had thick mud on the floor.
10. Perhaps we should move to higher ground.

Lesson 8 **Write *S* next to each simple sentence and *C* next to each compound sentence. Then circle each conjunction or semicolon in each compound sentence.**

1. Danny and Alicia went rafting on the Colorado River. _____
2. The first day the water was calm, and Danny and Alicia enjoyed the scenery. _____
3. At night they camped along the river bank, and the guides made a delicious dinner. _____
4. The next morning the weather had turned cloudy. _____
5. The river still looked calm, but the guides warned of dangerous rapids ahead. _____
6. The rafters entered a very difficult part of the river. _____
7. The raft shot past huge boulders and down small waterfalls; Danny and Alicia held on tightly. _____
8. The wild roller-coaster ride lasted only 30 seconds, but it was long enough for them. _____
9. Finally the raft reached calmer waters; everyone breathed a sigh of relief. _____
10. Danny and Alicia loved the experience. _____

Lesson 9 **Each sentence below has one independent clause and one dependent clause. Draw one line under each independent clause and two lines under each dependent clause. Then circle the subordinating conjunction that begins each dependent clause.**

1. Many people don't visit the desert because they are worried about its intense heat.
2. If you take proper precautions, you can enjoy a desert vacation.
3. Because summer heat is quite intense, you should plan your trip for the spring or fall.
4. Because it is hottest at noon, you should begin your desert exploration in the morning.
5. After the sun has set, the desert air grows cooler.
6. As the temperature drops, nocturnal animals come out in search of food.
7. Although most desert creatures are harmless, you must be cautious in open terrain.
8. Startled rattlesnakes sometimes attack, though they generally avoid people.
9. When you hike in the desert, you should always carry a snake-bite kit.
10. A desert vacation can be fun and safe when you put safety first.

Lesson 10 **Write *CX* next to each complex sentence. Underline the dependent clause.**

1. Although we've been to the park many times, we never get tired of it. ________
2. My favorite ride is the roller coaster, but I also enjoy the Ferris wheel. ________
3. Liz does not like these rides because she is afraid of heights. ________
4. While I fly high in the sky, she takes a spin on the merry-go-round. ________
5. This ride is a hundred years old, and its horses are beautifully carved. ________
6. It is the most popular attraction in the park. ________
7. After we have lunch at the hotdog stand, we usually get ice cream. ________
8. Then we ride the bumper cars, or we play some games. ________
9. I am especially good at the ring toss and at throwing darts. ________
10. When the sun begins to set, we head home tired but happy. ________

Extra Practice

Name ______________________________

Lesson 11 **Circle the first word in each boldfaced dependent clause. Write *RP* if it is a relative pronoun. Write *RA* if it is a relative adverb.**

1. The annual hiking trip is an event **that our class looks forward to.** ________
2. We travel by bus to a park **where there are several different habitats.** ________
3. We come across forests, prairies, and wetlands **when we hike.** ________
4. Mrs. Jensen, **who is a wildlife expert,** points out many animals. ________
5. She knows all the places **where birds, deer, and snakes like to hide.** ________
6. She can also identify tracks, **which is a good way to find animals.** ________
7. One counselor, Mr. Bates, is a botanist **who knows all about plants.** ________
8. He takes us to a meadow **where there are several kinds of wildflowers.** ________
9. He reminds us not to pick the flowers **when we are in a state park.** ________
10. It is important not to disturb plants **that grow naturally in a habitat.** ________

Lesson 12 **Write *F* next to each fragment, *RO* next to each run-on sentence, and *CS* next to each comma splice.**

1. While driving across Montana one dry summer. ________
2. We saw a herd of buffalo, we were amazed. ________
3. In 1889 only 551 buffalo remained in the United States most had been killed by hunters. ________
4. Extinction of the entire species. ________
5. Today more than fifteen thousand buffalo. ________
6. Most live on game preserves some run wild in national parks. ________
7. The buffalo we saw in Montana lived on a private ranch, they are raised for meat. ________
8. I have never eaten buffalo stew I'd like to try it. ________
9. The animals we saw are called American bison, most people call them buffalo. ________
10. These powerful, majestic animals. ________

Lesson 13 **Circle the common nouns. Underline the proper nouns.**

1. Langley Park is always crowded on holidays.
2. The fireworks attract people on the Fourth of July.
3. The Smiths arrive early at the park.
4. Janis and Nestor play baseball.
5. Savannah practices karate.
6. The outdoor pool opens in May.
7. My brother won the Best Swimmer Award.
8. His strength has helped make him the best swimmer in Nashville.
9. Labor Day signals that summer is over.
10. In September, we go back to school.

Lesson 14 **First put a box around each noun that is both plural and possessive. For the remaining nouns, underline each plural noun and circle each possessive noun.**

1. The dancers practiced for the Lunar New Year for many months.
2. Volunteers sewed the ornate red costumes.
3. The group's leader gave the signal to drum loudly.
4. The firecrackers' smoke filled the air.
5. The women's movements were graceful.
6. Boys and girls crowded closer to see the dancing lions.
7. One father tried to hush his baby's cries.
8. The lions' heads seemed to roar.
9. Several photographers ran out in front of the crowd.
10. Then the acrobats' performance began.

Extra Practice

Name ______________________________

Lesson 15 **Read each sentence. Circle the boldfaced word that is the type of noun listed in parentheses.**

1. "I can't think of a **topic** for my personal **essay**," complained Iris. (concrete noun)
2. "Have some **patience**. It will come to you," her **father** replied. (abstract noun)
3. "My mind is blank. I have no **ideas**!" Iris said with a **frown**. (abstract noun)
4. "You could write about being in the school **choir**," her **father** said. (collective noun)
5. "Describe the **joy** you feel when you sing that **song**," he suggested. (abstract noun)
6. Iris considered the **idea**, but then she shook her **head**. (concrete noun)
7. "I'd rather write a **paper** about joining the basketball **team**," she said. (collective noun)
8. "I have good **memories** of winning the championship **trophy**," she added. (abstract noun)
9. "Yes, remember the **crowd** that came to cheer you on?" her **father** asked. (collective noun)
10. "I think I have an **idea**!" Iris said as she picked up her **pencil**. (concrete noun)

Lesson 16 **Write a pronoun from the word bank that could take the place of the underlined word or phrase in each sentence. Remember to capitalize a word that begins a sentence.**

her	him	he	she	they	them	we

1. <u>Kate</u> always sings off key. __________
2. Kate's brothers and sisters complain about <u>Kate's</u> singing. __________
3. <u>Nora, Emily, Carl, and Matt</u> asked for ear plugs. __________
4. "<u>Your father and I</u> enjoy her singing," their mother replied. __________
5. "Then you share a room with her!" <u>Nora and Emily</u> said. __________
6. Kate's music teacher encouraged her to practice with <u>Luisa and Dawn</u>. __________
7. On the day of the spring concert <u>Kate's</u> family sat in the front row. __________
8. <u>Mr. Higashi</u> gave a welcoming speech to the students and guests. __________
9. A baby girl screamed happily at <u>Mr. Higashi</u>. __________
10. "<u>That baby</u> will be a member of our chorus someday!" said Mr. Higashi with a smile.
____

Lesson 17 **The verb in each sentence is underlined. Circle each action verb. Draw a box around each linking verb.**

1. The Baltimore and Ohio <u>is</u> one of the oldest railroads in the United States.
2. In the 1820s, cities <u>needed</u> ways to transport goods around the country.
3. Some <u>constructed</u> waterways for shipping called canals.
4. Baltimore <u>started</u> a rail line to the Ohio River in 1828.
5. Until 1830, most trains <u>were</u> horse-drawn vehicles.
6. Then a new steam-powered train <u>became</u> a common sight on the tracks.
7. In August 1830, this steam locomotive <u>carried</u> passengers to Ellicott's Mills.
8. The passengers <u>were</u> speechless when they sped along at 15 miles per hour.
9. According to legend, a horse-drawn car <u>raced</u> the train back to Baltimore.
10. Because of a broken part on the locomotive, the horse <u>was</u> the winner.

Lesson 18 **Circle the main verb in each sentence. Underline the helping verb.**

1. Many creative pieces were displayed at the student art show.
2. Anna's oil paintings were framed for the event.
3. Other landscapes were hung on the wall next to them.
4. Visitors could see Gus and Maria's clay vases.
5. They were dried in the big kiln in the art room.
6. Colin has carved little birds and mice out of wood for years.
7. His animals were arranged on a table near the front.
8. Lance's picture of his sister was drawn with charcoal.
9. It has received a special prize for the best piece at the show.
10. All the talented student artists should take a bow!

Name ______________________________

Lesson 19 **Underline the modal auxiliary in parentheses that best completes each sentence.**

1. Now that the rink is open for the winter, we (can/must) finally skate!
2. If you cannot find your ice skates, you (can/may) borrow my sister's.
3. I (must/can) ask for her permission first, of course.
4. We (could/must) go skating on Friday after school or on Saturday morning.
5. My mom (may/can) drive you if you do not have a ride.
6. Mom says you (could/should) tell your parents where you are going to be.
7. Do you think the skating rink (might/must) be really crowded?
8. I know it will be cold, so I (can/will) wear a hat and gloves.
9. I (may/must) even wear my new wool sweater with the snowflakes on it.
10. You (should/could) make sure to dress warmly as well.

Lesson 20 **Underline each adjective (including *a, an,* and *the*) in the sentences below.**

1. Sam has a small, shady garden.
2. Three golden carp swim in a pond.
3. The cat stares at them with sharp eyes.
4. Many flowers bloom in pots.
5. Some flowers are white and blue; others are yellow and red.
6. Butterflies land on the tall grass.
7. Sam digs in the dark, moist earth.
8. Slimy earthworms curl into tiny balls.
9. Hungry robins dive at the slithery worms.
10. Sam enjoys this tiny garden.

Lesson 21 Circle the adverb that describes each underlined word.

1. The alarm clock rang noisily in my ear.
2. I quickly rose and dressed myself.
3. I carefully checked the departure time on my airline ticket.
4. Planes rarely wait for tardy passengers.
5. My cat watched sadly as I ate breakfast.
6. The taxi driver honked the horn impatiently.
7. He drove fast, and I held my breath and closed my eyes.
8. When the driver stopped the taxi, I cautiously opened my eyes.
9. I paid him and tipped him generously.
10. I walked directly to the ticket counter and checked my baggage.

Lesson 22 Write the adjectives in parentheses in the correct order in each sentence.

1. Wyatt saw ______________________________ cars at the car show. (antique, seventy)
2. The ______________________________ cars were from the 1920s. (black, five, boxy)
3. The ______________________________ cars were made in the 1940s. (large, curvy)
4. A 1950s station wagon had ______________________________ panels. (wooden, smooth)
5. He really liked the ______________________________ cars from the 1960s. (sporty, red)
6. Some were convertibles with ______________________________ tops. (canvas, dark)
7. They also had ______________________________ wheels. (silver, shiny)
8. The ______________________________ cars from the 1970s were like boats. (rectangular, giant)
9. Many were painted a ______________________________ color. (dull, green)
10. ______________________________ cars had been used for racing. (small, colorful, three)

Extra Practice

Name ____________________

Lesson 23 **Underline each coordinating conjunction. Circle each subordinating conjunction.**

1. Tyler and Zoe decided to make homemade pizza.
2. They usually buy it at Giorgio's or the Hopkins Cafe.
3. They thought it would be easy to make, but they weren't sure how to make the crust.
4. Although Tyler is an experienced cook, he wanted to follow a recipe.
5. If the pizza turned out badly, they would be very disappointed.
6. One cookbook had recipes for pineapple pizza and pesto pizza.
7. Because Zoe loves pineapple, it was an easy choice.
8. They put the pizza in the oven and turned on their favorite TV show.
9. While they watched TV, the pizza baked.
10. Before they tasted the pizza, they let it cool.

Lesson 24 **Underline the pair of correlative conjunctions in each sentence.**

1. Neither Ryan nor Gina made it to school today.
2. They not only are suffering from coughs but also have fevers.
3. Tonight's play must go on, whether they recover or cannot perform.
4. Ross is both ready and willing to stand in for Ryan.
5. He not only knows Ryan's part but also has rehearsed it a few times.
6. Replacing Ryan at the last minute is both scary and exciting.
7. Mr. Suarez thinks either Jill or Becca could stand in for Gina.
8. Gina's role is neither large nor difficult to learn.
9. Tonight's performance will either go smoothly or have some flaws.
10. Whatever happens, Mr. Suarez will be both proud and nervous.

Lesson 25 **Underline the word in parentheses that will correctly complete each sentence.**

1. "Emi and her brother are going to Colorado for (their/there/they're) vacation," Kris said.
2. "I've never been (their/there/they're)," she added enviously.
3. "How are they getting (their/there/they're)?" asked Luis.
4. "(Their/There/They're) flying and then renting a car at the Denver airport," Kris replied.
5. "Do they need someone to water (their/there/they're) plants?" Luis asked.
6. "I live near (their/there/they're) house, so I could do it," he went on.
7. "I hope (their/there/they're) planning to take a lot of pictures," said Kris.
8. "Have you seen the pictures from (their/there/they're) trip to Georgia?" asked Luis.
9. "(Their/There/They're) lucky to be able to travel so much," sighed Kris.
10. "I don't envy (their/there/they're) travels. I like it here at home," said Luis.

Lesson 26 **Write *its* or *it's* on the line to complete each sentence correctly. Remember to capitalize a word that begins a sentence.**

1. "____________ called a tarantula," said Mr. Muñoz, holding up the large, hairy spider for the class to see.
2. "It makes ____________ home in warm areas around the world," he continued.
3. "____________ as big as my fist!" exclaimed Carlos.
4. "If you think this species is big, you should see the bird spider, which can spread ____________ legs about seven inches," said the teacher.
5. "____________ scary looking!" said Darrell.
6. "____________ really very friendly," said Mr. Muñoz, letting the spider walk up his arm.
7. "____________ bite can kill you!" shouted Alicia.
8. "____________ bite was once believed to cause a disease called *tarantism*," Mr. Muñoz explained.
9. "In reality, ____________ no more dangerous than a bee," he continued.
10. "There's an Australian tarantula that's much more dangerous than this one," he added. "____________ one of a group of tarantulas called *funnel-webs*."

Extra Practice

Extra Practice

Name ______________________________

Lesson 27 **Write *your* or *you're* to complete each sentence correctly. Remember to capitalize a word that begins a sentence.**

1. "Evie, may I borrow ______________ bike today?" asked Jason.
2. "Sure," said Evie, "but if ______________ going to the park, be sure to lock it up."
3. "______________ late," Juan called when Jason arrived.
4. "Do you want me to play on ______________ team or on Dean's team?" Jason asked.
5. "______________ going to play on my team," answered Juan.
6. "______________ playing well today," Juan said when Jason caught his second fly ball.
7. "______________ advice about staying on my toes has really helped," Jason responded.
8. After reviewing the lineup, Juan told Jason, "______________ up third, so get ready."
9. "______________ up at bat next," Juan said.
10. "Keep ______________ eye on the ball!" he yelled.

Lesson 28 **Underline the word in parentheses that correctly completes each sentence.**

1. My sister thinks that birds make the (best/goodest) pets.
2. I like dogs much (better/gooder) than birds.
3. Dogs are (better/gooder) at playing games than birds.
4. My dog Lucy used to be the (worsest/worst) behaved dog in the world.
5. I took her to obedience school, and her behavior became (gooder/better).
6. Now Lucy is the (best/goodest) student in the class!
7. She's getting (better/gooder) at following my commands.
8. My sister used to complain that Lucy's fur made her allergies (worse/worser).
9. Spring is the (worsest/worst) time of year for allergies.
10. Having a dog in the house does make some people's allergies (worse/worser).

Lesson 29 Write *who, which,* or *that* in the blank to complete each sentence correctly.

1. Halloween, _______________ takes place on October 31st, is my favorite holiday.
2. It's fun for children, _______________ get to dress up in costumes.
3. I like to wear costumes _______________ are wild and original.
4. My mother, _______________ is an artist, usually makes my costumes for me.
5. Last year I wore a dragon costume _______________ had a long tail and glittering scales.
6. My brother, _______________ is older than I, takes me trick-or-treating with him.
7. We only eat treats _______________ come wrapped in packages.
8. Last year my neighbor transformed her garage into a haunted house _______________ was very scary.
9. It had fake skeletons _______________ popped out from dark corners.
10. On Halloween night, my brother and I ate several pieces of candy, _______________ made me feel a little bit ill.

Lesson 30 Circle the word in parentheses that correctly completes each sentence.

1. My sister DeShawn is a (very/real) good horseback rider.
2. When my parents offered to pay for horseback riding lessons, she was (very/real) excited.
3. She showed (very/real) talent at the sport, even as a beginner.
4. She could ride horses that were usually (very/real) skittish with other riders.
5. She also practiced (very/real) hard.
6. DeShawn's riding instructor thought she could be a (very/real) champion someday, so she spent extra hours coaching her.
7. We were all (very/real) proud of DeShawn the day she won her first blue ribbon at a horse show.
8. Now she lives on a (very/real) horse farm and raises horses.
9. She is (very/real) lucky to be able to do something she loves.
10. I feel (very/real) happy whenever she asks me to visit.

Extra Practice

Name ______________________________

Lesson 31 **Write the correct form of *sit* or *set* in each blank.**

1. When I got home from school, I __________ my backpack down on the kitchen table.
2. After getting myself a snack, I __________ down at the table and pulled out my homework assignment.
3. "Jaime, can you please __________ somewhere else?" Mom asked.
4. I took my belongings up to my room, __________ them on my desk, and tried to start my homework again.
5. A little while later, my mother called, "Jaime, please come help me __________ the table."
6. I carefully __________ eight dinner plates around the table.
7. Then I __________ the napkins, knives, forks, and spoons in their proper places.
8. Just then my father came home and __________ a bag of groceries on the counter.
9. Mom __________ the food on the table while Dad put the groceries away.
10. Finally, we all __________ down and ate.

Lesson 32 **Underline the word in parentheses that correctly completes each sentence.**

1. Last summer my father took my sister to the pool to (learn/teach) her how to swim.
2. "First, I'm going to (learn/teach) you how to float on your back," he said to her.
3. My sister soon (learned/taught) that she could float without sinking.
4. After a few days he told her, "Now I'm going to (learn/teach) you some basic strokes."
5. First, he (learned/taught) her how to do the crawl.
6. "You need to (learn/teach) how to move your head correctly when you breathe," he said.
7. "When am I going to (learn/teach) how to dive?" my sister asked him.
8. "I'll (learn/teach) you to dive after you've learned how to swim well," he answered.
9. After that, my sister practiced hard and (learned/taught) her basic strokes very quickly.
10. By the end of the summer, my dad said she was ready to (learn/teach) how to do a swan dive.

Lesson 33 **Circle the word in parentheses that best completes each sentence.**

1. Kamika and I will get up early (to/two/too) make muffins for breakfast.
2. The recipe will yield over (to/two/too) dozen blueberry muffins.
3. We will need (to/two/too) cups of flour, milk, and eggs.
4. Is this bowl (to/two/too) small to mix all the ingredients?
5. Kamika will go out (to/two/too) the backyard and pick the blueberries.
6. She will wash them and fold them into the batter, (to/two/too).
7. The muffins will bake for at least thirty-(to/two/too) minutes.
8. We will be careful not to leave them in the oven (to/two/too) long.
9. They will still be warm when we bring them (to/two/too) the table.
10. I think I will eat at least (to/two/too) of these delicious treats.

Lesson 34 **Underline the word in parentheses that correctly completes each sentence.**

1. My aunt (knew/known) she wanted to be a policewoman when she was just a little girl.
2. "All my girlfriends wanted to be ballerinas or nurses when they (grew/grown) up," she said to me last week.
3. "I (knew/known) I did not want to dance or work in a hospital," she added.
4. She (grew/grown) up during a time when women didn't have as many job opportunities as they do today.
5. Many people she (knew/known) tried to discourage her from becoming a police officer.
6. "Luckily," she said, "I had (knew/known) several women who had interesting careers."
7. "I also (grew/grown) up in a family that encouraged me to follow my dreams," she added.
8. "I (knew/known) that being a girl wouldn't stop me from doing what I wanted to do," my aunt continued.
9. "You have (grew/grown) up in a time in which it's more acceptable for women to work in a variety of jobs," she told me.
10. I have (knew/known) many helpful people, but my aunt is the one who has encouraged me the most.

Extra Practice

Name ____

Lesson 35 **Read the boldfaced pronoun in each sentence. Write *RF* if it is a reflexive pronoun. Write *IN* if it is an indefinite pronoun.**

1. "I think we can teach **ourselves** how to surf," said Brad. ________
2. "It looks so simple that **anyone** can do it," he exclaimed. ________
3. "We should find **somebody** who can give us lessons," I warned. ________
4. Keeping balanced on a surfboard is not easy for **everyone.** ________
5. "You could hurt **yourself** if you don't know the right technique," I said. ________
6. "I guess there might be **something** an expert can show us," Brad replied. ________
7. "I would not want to make a fool of **myself** at the beach," he said with a laugh. ________
8. "Yes, and **nothing** is more important than being safe," I said. ________
9. I did not want Brad to get **himself** in trouble out in the water. ________
10. "So, do you know **someone** who can teach us how to surf?" asked Brad. ________

Lesson 36 **Circle the antecedent or antecedents of each boldfaced pronoun.**

1. The campers were ready for the annual canoe race. Any minute now **it** would begin.
2. Five canoes were at the starting line. **They** surged forward at the sound of the whistle.
3. At first, Lisa and Andre were in the lead. One by one the other teams passed **them.**
4. The blue canoe did not stay long enough in the race. **It** tipped over, and its paddlers had to pull the canoe ashore.
5. The lake was calm and smooth. The only waves on **it** were created by the racers.
6. Germaine and Jody were in the red canoe. **They** had won last year, and many people thought they would win again.
7. Lloyd and Veronica were way ahead of the others. The crowd of campers cheered **them** on.
8. The finish line was still many yards away. Who would cross **it** first?
9. Suddenly, Germaine and Jody began catching up. **They** paddled hard until they had passed Lloyd and Veronica.
10. The red canoe crossed the finish line first. Germaine and Jody clapped and cheered as **they** floated toward the shore.

Lesson 37 Circle each boldfaced word that is a subject pronoun. Underline each boldfaced word that is an object pronoun.

1. Yesterday **I** helped my grandmother clean out her attic. **It** was full of interesting things.
2. My grandfather died a long time ago. **We** found an old photo of **him**.
3. **He** was wearing a naval uniform in the picture, and he looked handsome to **us**.
4. Grandmother gave the photo to **me**. **She** said she had another copy in her album.
5. **We** dragged a huge trunk out from behind some boxes. Inside **it we** found a pile of old-fashioned clothes.
6. **They** had plastic wrapped around **them**. **They** were perfectly preserved.
7. There was a kimono my grandfather had brought back with **him** from Japan. **He** visited Asia in the 1970s.
8. **I** unwrapped a beautiful blue evening gown that had been my grandmother's. I asked **her** if she would try it on.
9. **She** laughed and said that none of the dresses would fit **her** anymore.
10. We wrapped up the dresses and put **them** back in the trunk. Grandmother said that when I was big enough, they would belong to **me**.

Lesson 38 Circle the correct pronoun in each pair.

1. Laney and (me/I) made a treasure hunt for my little brother and sister.
2. We drew chalk maps on the sidewalk for him and (she/her) to follow.
3. My little sister is a good treasure hunter, so Laney and (I/me) had to make her clues hard.
4. My little brother is only four, so I helped (he/him) with the clues.
5. (He/Him) and I walked all over the yard, following clues.
6. My little sister and Laney worked as a team, competing against my brother and (me/I).
7. When my brother and sister got close to the treasure, Laney and (me/I) stopped helping.
8. They begged Laney and (me/I) to give away the last few clues, but we held firm.
9. Finally, she and (him/he) decided to help each other find the treasure.
10. They thanked Laney and (me/I) when they found out that the treasure was a big bag of popcorn.

Extra Practice

Name ____

Lesson 39 **Underline the correct form of each verb in parentheses. Make sure the verb agrees with the subject.**

1. In the south of France farmers (grow/grows) flowers for French perfume.
2. The Battle of the Flowers (take/takes) place there every February.
3. This twelve-day festival (include/includes) a parade through the city of Nice.
4. The people of Nice (build/builds) beautiful floats for the parade.
5. They (use/uses) flowers to decorate the floats.
6. Many Battles of the Flowers (occur/occurs) during the festival.
7. Each battle (last/lasts) all afternoon.
8. People (bring/brings) lots of flowers to the battle.
9. At the signal, everyone (throw/throws) flowers at one another.
10. Soon, colored petals (cover/covers) the ground.

Lesson 40 **Underline the correct form of *be* in each sentence.**

1. Traffic lights (is/are) an important safety device.
2. Before the invention of the traffic signal in the early 1920s, drivers (was/were) free to cross an intersection at any time. This caused accidents.
3. Garrett Morgan (was/were) an African-American inventor.
4. His electric traffic signal system (was/were) the first of its kind.
5. One day Morgan saw a traffic accident in which several people (was/were) hurt.
6. Morgan (was/were) certain that he could improve traffic safety.
7. The modern traffic light system (is/are) only slightly different from Morgan's original system.
8. Today, this system (is/are) in operation all over the world.
9. Motorists everywhere (is/are) familiar with the traffic signal.
10. Driving (is/are) safer because of Morgan's invention.

Lesson 41 **The verb in each sentence is boldfaced. Circle each present tense verb. Underline each past tense verb. Draw a box around each future tense verb.**

1. Electric cars **use** energy stored in batteries instead of gasoline.
2. Many early cars **were** actually electric cars.
3. But gasoline-powered cars **became** popular in the early 1900s.
4. American companies **produced** them in large numbers.
5. They **remained** our car of choice for decades.
6. Critics **see** several problems with gasoline-powered cars, however.
7. Some day we **will run out** of the natural resources used to make gasoline.
8. And our cars' fumes **make** the air very dirty.
9. Electric cars **are** now ready to make a comeback.
10. They **will provide** a clean, reliable option for drivers for years to come.

Lesson 42 **The verb in each sentence is boldfaced. Circle each present progressive verb. Underline each past progressive verb. Draw a box around each future progressive verb.**

1. Aiden **is starting** a book club with a few of his friends.
2. They **will be meeting** every Saturday afternoon at three o'clock.
3. Aiden **was hoping** they could meet at the library, but it didn't work out.
4. Now he **is thinking** about inviting everyone to his house instead.
5. All the members **will be deciding** which books to read together.
6. Aiden **is trusting** that everyone will finish reading on time!
7. He **was expecting** that they'd begin with a novel, but they chose a play.
8. Although he prefers nonfiction, Aiden **is enjoying** the play.
9. He **is trying** his best to understand the characters and the theme.
10. He **will be leading** Saturday's discussion, so he must be prepared.

Extra Practice

Name ______________________________

Lesson 43 **Complete each sentence by writing the present perfect form of the verb (*has* or *have* plus the past participle) in parentheses. Watch for irregular verbs!**

1. Jessie ______________ model airplanes since she was eight. (fly)
2. Her dad ______________ model airplanes since he was a little boy. (love)
3. Their neighbors ______________ them how to fly model planes. (ask)
4. Jessie's mom ______________ a picnic lunch for the flying lesson. (pack)
5. "I ______________ that it may rain this morning," Jessie's mom warned. (hear)
6. "It ______________ every Saturday!" Jessie complained. (rain)
7. "You ______________ a long time to fly your plane," her father said. (wait)
8. "The neighbors ______________ for the park already," her mother said. (leave)
9. "Everyone ______________ to do this for a long time," Jessie pointed out. (want)
10. "I ______________ my decision," Jessie's mother said. "Let's go!" (reach)

Lesson 44 **Write the form of the verb that is described in parentheses to correctly complete each sentence.**

1. Mai ______________ her homework by four o'clock. (past perfect of *finish*)
2. She ______________ our dog Fluffy as well. (past perfect of *walk*)
3. By dinnertime, she ______________ her room. (past perfect of *clean*)
4. I ______________ only my math worksheet. (past perfect of *complete*)
5. I ______________ home late from soccer practice. (past perfect of *arrive*)
6. By bedtime, Mai ______________ several e-mails. (future perfect of *send*)
7. She ______________ her flute for an hour. (future perfect of *play*)
8. She ______________ a video on the computer. (future perfect of *watch*)
9. I ______________ to write my book report. (future perfect of *fail*)
10. Mai ______________ harder than I have again! (future perfect of *work*)

Name ________________________

Lesson 45 **Read each sentence. Are all the verb tenses correct, or is there an incorrect verb tense shift? Write *X* if the sentence contains an incorrect verb tense.**

1. When Jeff's dog Cindy ran away, he loses all hope of finding her. ______
2. Cindy had been missing for two days, and no one had seen her. ______
3. Jeff felt terrible because he is not watching her carefully at the park. ______
4. He had looked away only a minute, but she still will disappear. ______
5. His dad suggested that he put up flyers, but Jeff thought it was no use. ______
6. Just when Jeff believed the worst, he gets a call from a neighbor. ______
7. The man had found Cindy while he is jogging near the park! ______
8. Jeff was overjoyed, and he thanked the man over and over. ______
9. Now Jeff is not so hopeless when something bad happened. ______
10. He believes that things will usually turn out fine in the end. ______

Lesson 46 **Write *X* next to each sentence with two negative expressions. Then, on another sheet of paper, rewrite these sentences correctly.**

1. "I haven't seen nothing that looks familiar for hours," David told Geena. ______
2. "I haven't never been so lost in my life," Geena agreed. ______
3. "This wouldn't have happened if we had paid more attention to the road signs," David said.
4. "There isn't no reason to panic," Geena told David. ______
5. "I've never seen anyone look so confused," a police officer said to David.
6. "We didn't bring no map with us," David told the officer. ______
7. The officer told them not to have no worries. ______
8. "It won't take long to drive you back to your campsite," he said.
9. Police officers don't usually let no pedestrians ride in their police cars. ______
10. Geena and David had never ridden in no real police car before, and they accepted the offer. ______

Extra Practice

Name ____________________

Lesson 47 Underline the correct form of the adjective in parentheses.

1. Liza's dance troupe performed the (more creative/most creative) dance I have ever seen.
2. They combined ballet and gymnastics into a slow, balancing dance that was (most beautiful/more beautiful) than ballet alone.
3. Liza had designed the costumes, using the (lighter/lightest) fabric she could find.
4. The costumes flowed over the dancers' muscles, making them look (more graceful/gracefuler) than dancers in traditional leotards.
5. The music for their dance was (slowest/slower) than the music for the other dances.
6. Mia, the (smallest/smaller) girl in the whole company, amazed everyone.
7. She proved she was (strongest/stronger) than people thought by holding two dancers on her shoulders.
8. At the end of the piece, the applause was the (louder/loudest) I have ever heard.
9. Liza's dance troupe was definitely (better/best) than the other dance troupe.
10. They may be the (better/best) dance troupe in the city!

Lesson 48 Underline the correct form of the adverb.

1. Of all the swimmers at the starting line, Ellen waited the (most nervously/more nervously).
2. She had trained (hardest/harder) for this race than she had for any other race.
3. Ellen dove (more swiftly/most swiftly) than the swimmer next to her.
4. After falling behind in the first lap, Ellen came out of the turn (more quickly/most quickly) than any other swimmer in the race.
5. Her arms pulled her through the water, and soon she was swimming (more smoothly/most smoothly) than she had in the first lap.
6. Ellen's arms got tired (most easily/more easily) than her legs.
7. Still, she kept stroking (most persistently/more persistently) than she had in any other race.
8. Of all the people at the finish line, Ellen's dad cheered the (loudest/louder).
9. Ellen went home (most wearily/more wearily) than she ever had before.
10. Ellen ate the (most hungrily/more hungrily) at the dinner table that night.

Lesson 49 **Correct each capitalization and punctuation error. Then label each sentence *declarative, interrogative, imperative,* or *exclamatory*.**

1. please pass me the flour? ______________________
2. What are you making ______________________
3. I'm rolling out tortillas for dinner, ______________________
4. I love your homemade tortillas. ______________________
5. we are also having tamales for dinner and flan for dessert ______________________
6. is this a special occasion. ______________________
7. Yes, uncle Leo got a new job today? ______________________
8. what great news that is ______________________
9. don't tell anyone yet. ______________________
10. Is it a secret! ______________________

Lesson 50 **Draw three lines (≡) under each lowercase letter that should be capitalized. Draw a line through each uppercase letter that should not be capitalized.**

1. The washington Monument was built in honor of george washington.
2. It stands between the united states Capitol building and the lincoln memorial.
3. The potomac river is Nearby.
4. Funds for the Washington Monument were raised by the Washington national monument society.
5. The Tower was designed by robert mills.
6. The Walls of the tower are covered in White marble from maryland.
7. Many of the stones for the Washington monument were Donated.
8. Pope pius IX sent a Stone from the Temple of concord in rome, italy.
9. This stone was stolen one night by members of a Group called the Know-Nothings.
10. Today the Washington Monument is a National memorial and is maintained by the National park Service.

Extra Practice

Name ______________________________

Lesson 51 **Rewrite the items below on the lines. Use abbreviations where you can.**

1. Doctor Alison Reid Calloway ______________________
2. Tuesday, August 21 ______________________
3. Mister Mark Henry Novak ______________________
4. 333 Stone Avenue ______________________
5. The Hungry Dog Company ______________________
6. Doctor Martin Luther King Junior ______________________
7. Peachtree Boulevard ______________________
8. Piranhas Incorporated ______________________
9. Mister Joseph David Siegel ______________________
10. Friday, February 8 ______________________

Lesson 52 **Draw three lines (≡) under each letter in the sentence that should be capitalized.**

1. "Class, what should we do to celebrate presidents' day this year?" asked ms. carle.
2. "I'm confused," said mindy. "Isn't the holiday called washington's birthday?"
3. "Yes, it was begun to mark george washington's actual birthday on february 22," Ms. Carle replied.
4. "But in 1968 it was moved to the third monday of the month by the united states congress," she explained.
5. Ms. carle continued, "People thought the day could also honor other presidents, such as abraham lincoln."
6. "His birthday is also in february, isn't it?" said quinn. "So what is the holiday's real name?"
7. "In many states, such as massachusetts and connecticut, the official name, washington's birthday, is used," Ms. Carle said.
8. "But here in tennessee we call it presidents' day. Each state decides which name to use," she concluded.
9. "Let's serve chelsea's cherry delites and cherries from mel's groceries," suggested Lee.
10. "george washington did chop down a cherry tree, right?" said jordan. Ms. Carle just smiled.

Lesson 53 Circle the letters that should be capitalized in each title. Underline or add quotation marks to each title.

1. Sarita wrote a summary of a story titled legend of the okefenokee lizard.
2. Ami and Malvin went to the movie theater to see norton the alligator goes to france.
3. Jonas lent his book the poems of preston pig to his young cousin Emile.
4. Emile's favorite poem is called mud is magnificent.
5. What is the best story in the book titled trailside adventures?
6. Beware of the scorpion is my favorite story.
7. Neuri watched the movie tornado avengers with Alvin and Rami.
8. They loved the movie's theme song, the avengers are coming.
9. The librarian suggested Mari read the short story a girl of the south before traveling to Louisiana.
10. A magazine has decided to publish my poem frog music.

Lesson 54 Underline the correct word in each pair. If the word is a possessive, write *possessive.* If the word is a contraction, write the two words it was made from.

1. (Let's/Lets') go to the dog show. ____________________
2. The (rottweiler's/rottweilers') bodies are massive. ____________________
3. That (pug's/pugs') face is cute. ____________________
4. All (pug's/pugs') noses are stubby. ____________________
5. That (chow's/chows') tongue is black! ____________________
6. Look, (he's/hes') wagging his tail. ____________________
7. That is the biggest dog (Ive/I've) ever seen! ____________________
8. (It's/Its') an Irish wolfhound. ____________________
9. (Their/They're) the tallest of all breeds. ____________________
10. I think that one is the four (judge's/judges') favorite. ____________________

Name ____

Lesson 55 **Add commas where they belong. Circle commas that don't belong.**

1. This backpack has a, large inside pouch a small outside pouch, and, a hidden pocket.
2. Its special lining can, keep food hot warm or cold.
3. I can use it for hiking picnicking or school.
4. When I bring it to school, I keep, my lunch in the small pouch, my books in the big pouch and my keys, in the hidden pocket.
5. This backpack has belonged, to my uncle my cousin my brother, and me.
6. It has traveled to Africa Asia and Europe.
7. The places I've visited are, New Mexico, Canada and Oregon.
8. Right now I have pajamas a sleeping bag and my toothbrush in the backpack.
9. I'm going on a sleepover with Evan Michael Lucas and Josh.
10. We'll stay up late eat pizza and, tell scary stories.

Lesson 56 **Add the missing comma to each sentence. Then decide why the comma is needed. Write *I* for introductory word or element, *C* for compound sentence, and *D* for direct address.**

1. Dave do you know what that bridge is called? _____
2. No I have no idea. _____
3. I'll give you some hints and you guess its name. _____
4. Well I'll try to guess. _____
5. It was named after the channel it spans and the channel was named during the California Gold Rush. _____
6. Well does that mean the word *gold* is in the title? _____
7. Yes you're getting warm. _____
8. The second part of the name rhymes with *great* but there's no *r* in the word. _____
9. Mom don't give such easy clues! _____
10. Although you only gave me two clues I already know that it's the Golden Gate Bridge. _____

Lesson 57 **Add a semicolon where it is needed in each sentence.**

1. Soybeans come in many different colors they can be red, green, yellow, or speckled.
2. Soybeans are easy to grow they are a popular crop among farmers.
3. Soybean plants are good for the soil they provide nitrogen, an important nutrient.
4. Many foods are made from soybeans soy sauce, vegetable oil, soy flour, and tofu all have soy in them.
5. Soybeans can also be used for surprising things some fire extinguishers contain foam made from soy.
6. Tofu is made by boiling, crushing, and pressing soybeans this method was invented in China in 164 B.C.
7. The traditional Japanese diet includes tofu Japan imports large amounts of soybeans.
8. In Japan tofu is served in beautiful ways sometimes it is carved in the shape of leaves.
9. Tofu can be made to imitate many other foods it can even be made to taste like ice cream.
10. Tofu is a healthy food it provides more protein than lean beef.

Lesson 58 **Write *I* after each indirect quotation and *D* after each direct quotation. Then add quotation marks and other punctuation to the direct quotations.**

1. I'd like to have a garden, but I live in the city said Arno. _____
2. Dinah said that plants will grow well in a sunny window. _____
3. Arno opened the cupboard and asked Can I grow peas, beans, and peppers? _____
4. You can grow all of those things in containers Charlie said. _____
5. A bottle garden is another way to grow plants inside said Martha. _____
6. Martha explained that a bottle garden is called a *terrarium*. _____
7. First we need a big jar said Charlie. _____
8. Charlie said that Arno could put soil and plants in the jar. _____
9. What kind of small plants will you put in your terrarium asked Martha. _____
10. I think I'll put geraniums, moss, and ferns in it said Arno. _____

Name ____

Extra Practice

Lesson 59 **Add quotation marks and commas so that each direct quotation is written correctly.**

1. The new sculpture in front of Jefferson Public Library is the most creative art piece in the city says critic Melinda Lu.

2. Ms. Lu also writes The modern style may not appeal to everyone, but it really is a beautiful work.

3. In an editorial for the Jefferson Post, however, artist Jesse King writes I hardly think that *beautiful* is the best word to describe this thing.

4. Librarian Todd Hunt agrees. When I look out the window, all I see are ugly steel rods sticking up in the sky he writes in his blog.

5. Is it supposed to look like a bird, or maybe a giant butterfly? adds a confused visitor to the library.

6. The library's official statement about the sculpture says We are fully behind the artist and are proud to display his work to the public.

Lesson 60 **Rewrite this friendly letter correctly on the blanks below.**

Turkey Feather Ranch Peru, IN 46970 March 18, 20__ Dear Anya, My grandmother's ranch is so much fun! This morning, Grandma showed us where the baby turkeys grow. See you soon, Kristen

Read this text and answer the questions on the next page.

A Twister Is Formed

1 An unusually hot and humid afternoon in mid-May.
2 The sun has been shining but now there are storm clouds in the
3 west. Suddenly, your weather radio sounds a high-pitched alarm.
4 There is a tornado warning. You know it is time to take cover, but
5 do you know what is happening in the atmosphere around you?
6 Most likely, a large thunderstorm is approaching, the air
7 is very unstable. Warm air near the ground is rising and hitting
8 higher, cooler air. The water molecules in the warm air are in the
9 form of a gas. When those molecules rise and cool off; they
10 change into a liquid and fall as rain. Heat is also released when
11 the water molecules change. This causes updrafts, or strong
12 upward currents of air.
13 Something called wind shear is also present. Wind shear
14 is created when winds at different heights blow in different
15 directions or at different speeds. The varying wind speeds and
16 directions cause a tube of spinning air parallel to the ground.
17 Conditions are now perfect. For the formation of a tornado.
18 The updraft can pull on the spinning tube of air and make it
19 vertical. The tube tightens and spins faster it turns into a twister
20 capable of damaging anything in its path.

 Name ______________________

Read each item carefully. Fill in the circle next to the best answer.

1. **What change, if any, should be made to the underlined words in line 1?**
   - Ⓐ NO CHANGE
   - Ⓑ Is an unusually
   - Ⓒ Is an unusual
   - Ⓓ It is an unusually

2. **What change, if any, should be made to the underlined words in lines 2–3?**
   - Ⓐ NO CHANGE
   - Ⓑ shining, but now
   - Ⓒ shining, now
   - Ⓓ shining but, now

3. **What change, if any, should be made to the underlined words in lines 4–5?**
   - Ⓐ NO CHANGE
   - Ⓑ at the atmosphere
   - Ⓒ from the atmosphere
   - Ⓓ of the atmosphere

4. **What change, if any, should be made to the underlined words in lines 6–7?**
   - Ⓐ NO CHANGE
   - Ⓑ approaching the air
   - Ⓒ approaching. The air
   - Ⓓ approaching; The air

5. **What change, if any, should be made to the underlined words in lines 9–10?**
   - Ⓐ NO CHANGE
   - Ⓑ cool off. They
   - Ⓒ cool off? They
   - Ⓓ cool off, they

6. **What change, if any, should be made to the underlined words in lines 13–15?**
   - Ⓐ NO CHANGE
   - Ⓑ is created. When winds
   - Ⓒ is created which winds
   - Ⓓ is created, when winds

7. **What change, if any, should be made to the underlined words in line 17?**
   - Ⓐ NO CHANGE
   - Ⓑ perfect for the
   - Ⓒ perfect; for the
   - Ⓓ perfect, for the

8. **What change, if any, should be made to the underlined words in lines 19–20?**
   - Ⓐ NO CHANGE
   - Ⓑ faster, it turns
   - Ⓒ faster, but it turns
   - Ⓓ faster. It turns

Read each item carefully. Fill in the circle next to the best answer.

9. Read the following sentences.

> The shark swam gracefully around the tank. Only the glass separated it from us.

What part of the sentence is underlined?

(A) complete subject
(B) complete predicate
(C) simple subject
(D) simple predicate

10. Read the following sentences.

> The full moon shone very brightly. It was more like day than night!

What part of the sentence is underlined?

(A) complete subject
(B) complete predicate
(C) simple subject
(D) simple predicate

11. Read the following sentences.

> I'm surprised Kyle did not win the writing contest. His story was hilarious!

What part of the sentence is underlined?

(A) direct object
(B) indirect object
(C) predicate noun
(D) predicate adjective

12. Read the following sentences.

> Fossils are the remains of animals preserved in rock. They give people an idea of what ancient species looked like.

What part of the sentence is underlined?

(A) direct object
(B) indirect object
(C) predicate noun
(D) predicate adjective

13. Read the following paragraph.

> [1] The skin is the body's largest organ. [2] It protects you. [3] It keeps you warm. [4] Your skin is important, so keep it healthy.

What is the best way to combine sentences 2 and 3?

(A) It protects you, and keeps you warm.
(B) It protects you and keeps you warm.
(C) It protects you, it keeps you warm.
(D) It protects you but keeps you warm.

14. Read the following sentences.

> The ants crawled _____. There must have been hundreds of them!

Which is a prepositional phrase that completes the first sentence?

(A) and gathered together
(B) across the floor
(C) when the light hit them
(D) frantically

Name ______________________

Read each item carefully. Fill in the circle next to the best answer.

15. Read the following sentences.

> Is this the beach where you found that sand dollar? Let's dig around in the sand.

What kind of word is underlined?

- Ⓐ direct object
- Ⓑ relative pronoun
- Ⓒ predicate adjective
- Ⓓ relative adverb

16. Read the following sentences.

> Lydia will keep studying until she has learned all the words. She wants to win the spelling bee.

What part of the sentence is underlined?

- Ⓐ dependent clause
- Ⓑ independent clause
- Ⓒ complete predicate
- Ⓓ prepositional phrase

17. Read the following paragraph.

> [1] We can't wait to visit Grandma in Tucson. [2] It is still freezing here, but Arizona is warm and sunny. [3] We will see cacti and many desert animals. [4] Before we leave, Grandma will take us to the Arizona-Sonora Desert Museum.

Which sentence is a compound sentence?

- Ⓐ Sentence 1
- Ⓑ Sentence 2
- Ⓒ Sentence 3
- Ⓓ Sentence 4

18. Read the following paragraph.

> [1] Although she loves dogs, Missy prefers cats. [2] The thing Missy likes most about felines is that they are proud and quiet. [3] They are also easy to care for.

Where is the best place to add the following sentence?

> They do not run wildly and bark like dogs.

- Ⓐ Before sentence 1
- Ⓑ After sentence 1
- Ⓒ After sentence 2
- Ⓓ After sentence 3

19. Read the following sentence.

> Pedro sings in the local children's _____ once a week.

Which words and punctuation best complete the sentences?

- Ⓐ choir, they practice
- Ⓑ choir. They practice.
- Ⓒ choir. Practice
- Ⓓ choir. They practice

20. Read the following sentences.

> The engine sputtered and died, the car wouldn't start again. Mom went inside to call the mechanic.

Why is the first sentence incorrect?

- Ⓐ It is a fragment.
- Ⓑ It is a run-on sentence.
- Ⓒ It should be a question.
- Ⓓ It is a comma splice.

Read this text and answer the questions on the next page.

Daedalus and Icarus

1 Long ago, the cruel King Minos ruled the island of crete.
2 A ferocious monster called the Minotaur, who was half man and
3 half bull, terrorized its people. King Minos demanded that his
4 master craftsman, Daedalus, build a kind of maze called a labyrinth
5 to trap the Minotaur. The monster was lured to the maze and
6 trapped, but that was not enough for King Minos. He began to
7 throw his enemies in the labyrinth, where they would meet a
8 horribly end at the hands of the imprisoned monster.
9 King Minos did not want Daedalus to reveal the way out
10 of the maze. So he locked Daedalus and his son Icarus in a tower.
11 Father and son longed for escape. From their lofty window, he
12 looked with envy upon the birds flying free. Then one day Daedalus
13 had a brilliant idea. He and Icarus would fly from the tower just
14 like the birds. He will build them wings out of feathers and wax.
15 Daedalus soon completed the wings and gave Icarus his
16 pair with a warning. "Do not fly too close to the sun," he said.
17 Daedalus and Icarus jumped from the window, flapped
18 their white new delicate wings, and began to fly. Icarus ignored his
19 father's advice and boldly neared the sun. Daedalus watched in
20 horror as his sons wings melted and foolish Icarus fell into the sea.

Name ______________________________

Read each item carefully. Fill in the circle next to the best answer.

1. **What change, if any, should be made to the underlined words in line 1?**

   Ⓐ NO CHANGE
   Ⓑ Island of crete
   Ⓒ Island Of Crete
   Ⓓ island of Crete

2. **What change, if any, should be made to the underlined words in lines 2–3?**

   Ⓐ NO CHANGE
   Ⓑ terrorized its person's.
   Ⓒ terrorized its people's.
   Ⓓ terrorized its person.

3. **What change, if any, should be made to the underlined words in lines 6–8?**

   Ⓐ NO CHANGE
   Ⓑ meet a horrible end
   Ⓒ horrible meet an end
   Ⓓ meet an end horrible

4. **What change, if any, should be made to the underlined words in line 10?**

   Ⓐ NO CHANGE
   Ⓑ its son Icarus
   Ⓒ him son Icarus
   Ⓓ their son Icarus

5. **What change, if any, should be made to the underlined words in lines 11–12?**

   Ⓐ NO CHANGE
   Ⓑ their looked with envy
   Ⓒ they looked with envy
   Ⓓ him looked with envy

6. **What change, if any, should be made to the underlined words in line 14?**

   Ⓐ NO CHANGE
   Ⓑ He can build
   Ⓒ He may build
   Ⓓ He would build

7. **What change, if any, should be made to the underlined words in lines 17–18?**

   Ⓐ NO CHANGE
   Ⓑ delicate new white wings
   Ⓒ new delicate white wings
   Ⓓ white delicate new wings

8. **What change, if any, should be made to the underlined words in lines 19–20?**

   Ⓐ NO CHANGE
   Ⓑ his sons' wings
   Ⓒ his son's wings
   Ⓓ his sons's wings

Read each item carefully. Fill in the circle next to the best answer.

9. Read the following sentences.

The sun was setting as we sped down the highway. We still had hope that we would get to Denver before dark.

What kind of noun is underlined?

- Ⓐ proper
- Ⓑ possessive
- Ⓒ collective
- Ⓓ abstract

10. Read the following sentences.

It was a hot day on the ranch. A herd of cattle gathered in a shady corner of the pasture.

What kind of noun is underlined?

- Ⓐ proper
- Ⓑ possessive
- Ⓒ collective
- Ⓓ abstract

11. Read the following sentences.

Through a process called molting, birds shed _____ feathers and grow new ones. This happens at least once a year.

Which pronoun best completes the first sentence?

- Ⓐ them
- Ⓑ they
- Ⓒ her
- Ⓓ their

12. Read the following sentences.

We were exhausted after our five-mile hike. We collapsed onto the soft grass and had a rest.

What kind of verb is underlined?

- Ⓐ action
- Ⓑ linking
- Ⓒ concrete
- Ⓓ helping

13. Read the following paragraph.

[1] We are having a used book sale on Saturday. [2] All money raised will be donated to the local food pantry. [3] We have organized many fundraisers for the food pantry through the years.

Where is the best place to add the following sentence?

Last year's car wash was a big hit.

- Ⓐ Before sentence 1
- Ⓑ After sentence 1
- Ⓒ After sentence 2
- Ⓓ After sentence 3

14. Read the following sentences.

Taylor _____ try harder to get to practice on time. Doesn't he know the whole team is counting on him?

Which helping verb best completes the first sentence?

- Ⓐ might
- Ⓑ may
- Ⓒ should
- Ⓓ can

15. Read the following sentences.

Sophia often takes this shortcut through the park. She can make it home in only five minutes.

What kind of word is underlined?

- Ⓐ noun
- Ⓑ verb
- Ⓒ adjective
- Ⓓ adverb

Name ______________________________

Read each item carefully. Fill in the circle next to the best answer.

16. Read the following sentences.

I can't reach those storage boxes on the top shelf. Do you have a step ladder?

What kind of word is underlined?

Ⓐ noun
Ⓑ verb
Ⓒ adjective
Ⓓ adverb

17. Read the following sentences.

We will need a ____ pan to bake the casserole. Let's find it before we begin to mix the ingredients.

Which series of adjectives completes the first sentence and is in the correct order?

Ⓐ glass large rectangular
Ⓑ large rectangular glass
Ⓒ rectangular large glass
Ⓓ large glass rectangular

18. Read the following sentences.

[1] Kurt might research electricity for his science project. [2] He might build a model of the solar system. [3] He is interested in both subjects.

What is the best way to combine sentences 1 and 2?

Ⓐ Kurt might research electricity for his science project, or he might build a model of the solar system.
Ⓑ Kurt might research electricity for his science project, although he might build a model of the solar system.
Ⓒ Kurt might research electricity for his science project, he might build a model of the solar system.
Ⓓ Kurt might research electricity, or for his science project, he might build a model of the solar system.

19. Read the following paragraph.

[1] The Pony Express began in 1861. [2] Its messengers rode on horseback to carry mail between Missouri and California. [3] Pony Express riders were known for their speed. [4] Though the service was reliable, the Pony Express lasted for only a year.

Which sentence contains a subordinating conjunction?

Ⓐ Sentence 1
Ⓑ Sentence 2
Ⓒ Sentence 3
Ⓓ Sentence 4

20. Read the following sentences.

Neither the drizzle ____ the chilly breeze kept people from attending the picnic. Everyone showed up with umbrellas and raincoats.

Which correlative conjunction best completes the first sentence?

Ⓐ or
Ⓑ and
Ⓒ nor
Ⓓ but

Read this text and answer the questions on the next page.

To the Editor

1 There has been much debate lately concerning Westlake
2 Elementary's decision to require students to wear school uniforms.
3 In particular, Mr. Cleary's fifth-grade class has been real angry
4 about the new rule. They argue that forcing all students to dress
5 alike will rob them of the chance to be creative and unique. This
6 is a good point, but I think there are some gooder reasons to
7 get behind school uniforms.
8 The fifth-graders should remember that we are attending
9 school to teach, not to walk in a fashion show. Students should be
10 concentrating on math and science. They should not be wondering
11 who has the latest name-brand jeans as they set at their desks.
12 Likewise, time spent putting together the perfect outfit is wasted
13 time. When everyone is dressed alike, there are no distractions.
14 Students are free to think only of they're studies.
15 The most good argument for school uniforms is that they
16 create equality in the classroom. No students are more "in style"
17 or more privileged than others. No one will be teased about what
18 he or she is wearing. If all students look the same, it will be easier
19 for them to respect and relate to each other. Bullying will not be
20 such a worry. Doesn't that sound like a positive step for Westlake?

Name ______________________________

Read each item carefully. Fill in the circle next to the best answer.

1. What change, if any, should be made to the underlined words in lines 3–4?

Ⓐ NO CHANGE
Ⓑ has been well angry
Ⓒ has been right angry
Ⓓ has been very angry

2. What change, if any, should be made to the underlined words in lines 5–7?

Ⓐ NO CHANGE
Ⓑ some better reasons
Ⓒ some best reasons
Ⓓ some more good reasons

3. What change, if any, should be made to the underlined words in lines 8–9?

Ⓐ NO CHANGE
Ⓑ school to be learned
Ⓒ school to learn
Ⓓ school to be teached

4. What change, if any, should be made to the underlined words in lines 10–11?

Ⓐ NO CHANGE
Ⓑ sit at their desks
Ⓒ sat at their desks
Ⓓ setting at their desks

5. What change, if any, should be made to the underlined words in line 13?

Ⓐ NO CHANGE
Ⓑ When anyone is
Ⓒ When themselves is
Ⓓ When no one is

6. What change, if any, should be made to the underlined words in line 14?

Ⓐ NO CHANGE
Ⓑ of there studies
Ⓒ of these studies
Ⓓ of their studies

7. What change, if any, should be made to the underlined words in lines 15–16?

Ⓐ NO CHANGE
Ⓑ The most better argument
Ⓒ The goodest argument
Ⓓ The best argument

8. What change, if any, should be made to the underlined words in lines 18–19?

Ⓐ NO CHANGE
Ⓑ easier for they
Ⓒ easier for him
Ⓓ easier for we

Read each item carefully. Fill in the circle next to the best answer.

9. Read the following sentences.

I can't believe _____ going to miss the carnival. It will be so much fun!

Which word best completes the first sentence?

- Ⓐ you
- Ⓑ your
- Ⓒ you's
- Ⓓ you're

10. Read the following sentences.

The days were getting cooler and shorter. The trees were beginning to lose _____ leaves.

Which word best completes the second sentence?

- Ⓐ there
- Ⓑ their
- Ⓒ they're
- Ⓓ its

11. Read the following sentences.

The lion stalks _____ prey in the early morning hours. It hunts zebras, buffalo, and gazelles.

Which word best completes the first sentence?

- Ⓐ it's
- Ⓑ its
- Ⓒ their
- Ⓓ they're

12. Read the following sentences.

Jarrod is a boy _____ sits next to me in music class. He also lives in my neighborhood.

Which word best completes the first sentence?

- Ⓐ that
- Ⓑ which
- Ⓒ who
- Ⓓ he

13. Read the following paragraph.

[1] Jane thinks this is the best book the author has ever written. [2] She would argue that it is even better than his last novel. [3] Ivy does not agree at all. [4] In fact, she thinks it is the worse book she has ever read!

Which sentence contains an adjective that is incorrect?

- Ⓐ Sentence 1
- Ⓑ Sentence 2
- Ⓒ Sentence 3
- Ⓓ Sentence 4

14. Read the following sentences.

Elizabeth has _____ an inch since last year. She is the tallest girl in her class.

Which word best completes the first sentence?

- Ⓐ grown
- Ⓑ growed
- Ⓒ grew
- Ⓓ grows

15. Read the following sentences.

In the 1890s, millions of people came _____ America from Europe. Immigration was at an all-time high.

Which word best completes the first sentence?

- Ⓐ to
- Ⓑ threw
- Ⓒ too
- Ⓓ two

Name ______________________________

Read each item carefully. Fill in the circle next to the best answer.

16. **Read the following sentences.**

    > There were only ten seconds left in the game. The team _____ there was no hope for a victory.

    Which word best completes the second sentence?

    (A) knows
    (B) known
    (C) knowed
    (D) knew

17. **Read the following sentences.**

    > Mr. Lorenzo _____ me how to throw a curveball. I'm ready to try out for the baseball team.

    Which word best completes the first sentence?

    (A) teached
    (B) taught
    (C) learned
    (D) learns

18. **Read the following paragraph.**

    > [1] Anna studied her science notes for two hours. [2] John also studied for tomorrow's science test. [3] He completed a writing assignment as well.

    Where is the best place to add the following sentence?

    > She is prepared for the test tomorrow.

    (A) Before sentence 1
    (B) After sentence 1
    (C) After sentence 2
    (D) After sentence 3

19. **Read the following sentences.**

    > "We've locked <u>ourselves</u> out of the house," Dad said with a chuckle. "I'll call Uncle Rick and ask him to bring the spare key."

    What kind of pronoun is underlined?

    (A) indefinite
    (B) possessive
    (C) reflexive
    (D) relative

20. **Read the following sentences.**

    > [1] It was too cold to play outside. [2] Darren spent the afternoon finishing his book report. [3] His mom was proud of him for making good use of his time.

    What is the best way to combine sentences 1 and 2?

    (A) It was too cold to play outside, and Darren spent the afternoon finishing his book report.
    (B) It was too cold to play outside when Darren spent the afternoon finishing his book report.
    (C) It was too cold to play outside, but Darren spent the afternoon finishing his book report.
    (D) Since it was too cold to play outside, Darren spent the afternoon finishing his book report.

Read this text and answer the questions on the next page.

Escaping the Dust

1 “Do we really have to leave, Papa?” I asked. The old car
2 was packed to the gills with all our belongings. My little sister Kay
3 sat quietly in the back seat beside a frying pan and a pile of sheets.
4 Her silence was strange. She was only three, but she seems to
5 understand how sad and serious this day was for us.
6 It were the summer of 1935. The drought had ruined yet
7 another year’s crops. We had see so many dust storms blow
8 through our tiny Oklahoma town that they were now a grim fact
9 of life instead of a rare event. It’s hard to explain just how terrible
10 a dust storm is. A dark, sinister cloud—the darker cloud you’ve
11 ever seen—appears on the horizon. Then you have only minutes
12 to take shelter and shut all the doors and windows as tightly as
13 possible. Day turns into night as the dust blocks the sun. Then
14 the dust works its way into every possible crack and crevice of
15 your house. It coats the floor, the furniture, and the dishes. It
16 covers your clothes and skin. You taste the grit in your mouth.
17 “There’s not nothing left for us here, Liza,” Papa replied.
18 “The wheat is failing again. The land has nothing left to give.”
19 California sounded like a paradise where a farmer could
20 earn a good living. We have no choice but to head west.

Unit 4 Posttest

Name ______________________________

Read each item carefully. Fill in the circle next to the best answer.

1. What change, if any, should be made to the underlined words in lines 4–5?

   (A) NO CHANGE
   (B) but she seemed
   (C) but she is seeming
   (D) but she will seem

2. What change, if any, should be made to the underlined words in line 6?

   (A) NO CHANGE
   (B) It was the
   (C) It be the
   (D) It is the

3. What change, if any, should be made to the underlined words in lines 7–9?

   (A) NO CHANGE
   (B) We will have seen
   (C) We have seen
   (D) We had seen

4. What change, if any, should be made to the underlined words in lines 10–11?

   (A) NO CHANGE
   (B) the darkest cloud
   (C) the more dark cloud
   (D) the most darkly cloud

5. What change, if any, should be made to the underlined words in line 13?

   (A) NO CHANGE
   (B) Day turn into
   (C) Day turned into
   (D) Day have turned into

6. What change, if any, should be made to the underlined words in line 17?

   (A) NO CHANGE
   (B) There's anything left
   (C) There's nothing not left
   (D) There's nothing left

7. What change, if any, should be made to the underlined words in line 18?

   (A) NO CHANGE
   (B) wheat had been failing
   (C) wheat was failing
   (D) wheat is failed

8. What change, if any, should be made to the underlined words in line 20?

   (A) NO CHANGE
   (B) We has no
   (C) We had no
   (D) We are having no

Read each item carefully. Fill in the circle next to the best answer.

9. Read the following sentences.

> Today, Dad made lunch for _____. We had turkey sandwiches and apple slices.

Which words best complete the first sentence?

- (A) Kevin and I
- (B) Kevin and me
- (C) me and Kevin
- (D) I and Kevin

10. Read the following sentences.

> The librarian gave Jason a stern look. She told <u>him</u> to keep his voice down.

What kind of pronoun is underlined?

- (A) subject
- (B) reflexive
- (C) indefinite
- (D) object

11. Read the following sentences.

> Delaware is known as The First State. It _____ the first state to approve the U.S. Constitution in 1787.

Which form of the verb *be* best completes the second sentence?

- (A) is
- (B) are
- (C) was
- (D) were

12. Read the following paragraph.

> [1] Last week, the class wrote poems about nature. [2] Li Min enjoyed the assignment because she loves poetry. [3] Li Min will not have as much fun writing nonfiction.

Where is the best place to add the following sentence?

> Next week, the class will begin their research reports.

- (A) Before sentence 1
- (B) After sentence 1
- (C) After sentence 2
- (D) After sentence 3

13. Read the following sentences.

> Katie has been given the lead in the school musical. She _____ a girl who is lost in a forest.

Which word best completes the second sentence?

- (A) played
- (B) was playing
- (C) play
- (D) will be playing

14. Read the following sentences.

> Martha's aunt <u>has worked</u> at the hospital for ten years. She runs medical tests in the lab.

What verb form is underlined?

- (A) past progressive
- (B) present progressive
- (C) past perfect
- (D) present perfect

Name ____________________

Read each item carefully. Fill in the circle next to the best answer.

15. Read the following sentences.

By the time this day is over, the troop _____ almost six miles. They will be ready for a rest.

Which verb best completes the first sentence?

(A) had hiked
(B) will have hiked
(C) was hiking
(D) will be hiking

16. Read the following sentences.

Kirsten _____ she knew in the crowd. She felt totally alone.

Which words best complete the first sentence?

(A) didn't see no one
(B) didn't see anyone
(C) didn't not see anyone
(D) didn't see none

17. Read the following paragraph.

[1] Abraham Lincoln was born in Kentucky in 1809. [2] Though he grew up on the frontier, he still found time to read. [3] He becomes a lawyer in 1836. [4] He was elected president of the United States in 1860.

Which sentence contains an incorrect verb tense?

(A) Sentence 1
(B) Sentence 2
(C) Sentence 3
(D) Sentence 4

18. Read the following sentences.

Jenny dove deeper into the lake than Harry did. She found a shiny pebble at the bottom.

What kind of word is underlined?

(A) comparative adjective
(B) superlative adjective
(C) comparative adverb
(D) superlative adverb

19. Read the following sentences.

This is the _____ intersection in town. There have been two accidents here just this week.

Which word or words best complete the first sentence?

(A) dangerouser
(B) more dangerous
(C) most dangerous
(D) dangerest

20. Read the following sentences.

[1] Today's soccer practice was long and hard. [2] Faye was never happier to see her own bed. [3] She dropped her backpack on the floor. [4] She leapt into her bed.

What is the best way to combine sentences 3 and 4?

(A) She dropped her backpack on the floor after she leapt into her bed.
(B) She dropped her backpack on the floor and leapt into her bed.
(C) She dropped her backpack on the floor, and leapt into her bed.
(D) She dropped her backpack on the floor while leaping into her bed.

Read this text and answer the questions on the next page.

Local Shelter to Hold Fundraising and Adoption Event

1 Volunteers from the Furry Friends Dog Shelter will be
2 washing cars for a cause this Saturday from noon to six in the
3 parking lot of Frank's gourmet foods. All proceeds from the
4 event will go toward food supplies, and upkeep of the shelter.
5 Furry Friends will also bring along a few of their most adoptable
6 dogs and puppies for families considering a canine companion.
7 The car wash is the third fundraiser Furry Friends has
8 organized this year, according to its director, Dr Marla A Simms.
9 The March bake sale and June's silent auction were successful,
10 but the shelter still urgently needs funds to keep operating.
11 "Last year we lost the support of two big donors, so
12 every penny counts Dr. Simms explained. "Our cages are
13 almost always full, and it costs a lot to care for these animals."
14 And speaking of the animals, there will be some
15 wonderful dogs available for adoption this weekend. "We ll be
16 bringing some cute puppies, but please consider giving a home
17 to an older dog," Dr. Simms added. "We have a sweet five-year-
18 old German shepherd that would be the perfect pet."
19 Furry Friends is requesting a ten-dollar donation for
20 each car washed! Canine adoptions start at fifty dollars.

 Name ______________________

Read each item carefully. Fill in the circle next to the best answer.

1. What change, if any, should be made to the underlined words in lines 1–3?

   Ⓐ NO CHANGE
   Ⓑ frank's gourmet foods
   Ⓒ Frank's Gourmet foods
   Ⓓ Frank's Gourmet Foods

2. What change, if any, should be made to the underlined words in lines 3–4?

   Ⓐ NO CHANGE
   Ⓑ food, supplies, and upkeep
   Ⓒ food, supplies and, upkeep
   Ⓓ food supplies and upkeep

3. What change, if any, should be made to the underlined words in lines 7–8?

   Ⓐ NO CHANGE
   Ⓑ Dr. Marla A Simms
   Ⓒ Dr. Marla a. Simms
   Ⓓ Dr. Marla A. Simms

4. What change, if any, should be made to the underlined words in lines 9–10?

   Ⓐ NO CHANGE
   Ⓑ were successful but
   Ⓒ were successful but,
   Ⓓ were, successful but

5. What change, if any, should be made to the underlined words in lines 11–12?

   Ⓐ NO CHANGE
   Ⓑ counts, Dr. Simms explained. "
   Ⓒ counts." Dr. Simms explained.
   Ⓓ counts," Dr. Simms explained.

6. What change, if any, should be made to the underlined words in lines 15–17?

   Ⓐ NO CHANGE
   Ⓑ We'll be bringing
   Ⓒ Well' be bringing
   Ⓓ W'ill be bringing

7. What change, if any, should be made to the underlined words in lines 17–18?

   Ⓐ NO CHANGE
   Ⓑ Five-year-old German Shepherd
   Ⓒ Five-year-old german shepherd
   Ⓓ five-year-old german shepherd

8. What change, if any, should be made to the underlined words in lines 19–20?

   Ⓐ NO CHANGE
   Ⓑ each car washed?
   Ⓒ each car washed.
   Ⓓ each car washed,

Read each item carefully. Fill in the circle next to the best answer.

9. Read the following sentences.

> Where should we go on vacation this year? I would rather hike in the mountains than sit on a beach.

What kind of sentence is underlined?

- (A) declarative
- (B) interrogative
- (C) imperative
- (D) exclamatory

10. Read the following sentences.

> "I didn't know that canadian money was different from ours," said Tim. "We'll have to exchange our dollars in Toronto."

Which underlined word should be capitalized?

- (A) canadian
- (B) money
- (C) ours
- (D) dollars

11. Read the following sentences.

> Have you heard Maya read _____? It is the first poem she ever wrote.

Which is the correct title that completes the first sentence?

- (A) "Ants on the March"
- (B) Ants on the March
- (C) "Ants On The March"
- (D) Ants On The March

12. Read the following sentences.

> The Sahara Desert stretches across most of North Africa. It is almost the size of our entire Country.

Which underlined word should not be capitalized?

- (A) Sahara
- (B) Desert
- (C) Africa
- (D) Country

13. Read the following sentences.

> The wind on the pier suddenly picked up. All the _____ hats blew off their heads.

Which word best completes the second sentence?

- (A) woman's
- (B) womans'
- (C) women's
- (D) womens'

14. Read the following paragraph.

> [1] Wow, I can't wait to go to the water park tomorrow! [2] Brett are you excited, too? [3] I've already packed my swimsuit, towel, and sunscreen. [4] I've never been on the tallest waterslide, but I might try it this time!

Which sentence is missing a comma?

- (A) Sentence 1
- (B) Sentence 2
- (C) Sentence 3
- (D) Sentence 4

Name ____________________

Read each item carefully. Fill in the circle next to the best answer.

15. Read the following sentences.

"You forgot to feed the dog this morning didn't you?" said Mom with a frown. It was the second time I had forgotten that week.

Where should a comma be placed in the sentences?

(A) after *You*
(B) after *morning*
(C) after *said*
(D) after *forgotten*

16. Read the following friendly letter heading.

863 Green Tree Rd.
____
August 6, 2014

Which address will correctly complete the heading?

(A) Springfield IL 62704
(B) Springfield IL, 62704
(C) Springfield, IL 62704
(D) Springfield, IL, 62704

17. Read the following sentences.

The rain was relentless it sounded like a million fists pounding on the roof. I knew I would get no sleep that night.

Where should a semicolon be placed in the sentences?

(A) after *was*
(B) after *relentless*
(C) after *fists*
(D) after *get*

18. Read the following sentences.

The rule book _____ who draws the highest number goes first." Because she drew an eight, Bridget will begin the game.

Which words and punctuation correctly complete the first sentence?

(A) says, "The player
(B) says "The player
(C) says, the player
(D) says the player

19. Read the following paragraph.

[1] The announcement was a welcome one. [2] The class breathed a collective sigh of relief. [3] No one was prepared for the spelling test that day.

Where is the best place to add the following sentence?

"I have decided to postpone the test," said Mr. Reed.

(A) Before sentence 1
(B) After sentence 1
(C) After sentence 2
(D) After sentence 3

20. Read the following sentences.

[1] Karima put a lot of effort into her science project. [2] It took lots of planning. [3] It took several weekends to complete.

What is the best way to combine sentences 2 and 3?

(A) It took lots of planning and several weekends to complete.
(B) It took lots of planning and it took several weekends to complete.
(C) It took lots of planning, and several weekends to complete.
(D) It took lots of planning, or it took several weekends to complete.

Grammar, Usage, and Mechanics Handbook Table of Contents

Mechanics

Section 1 Capitalization

- **Capitalize the first word in a sentence.**
  The kangaroo rat is an amazing animal.
- **Capitalize all *proper nouns,* including people's names and the names of particular places.**
  Gregory Gordon   Washington Monument
- **Capitalize titles of respect.**
  Mr. Alvarez   Dr. Chin   Ms. Murphy
- **Capitalize family titles used just before people's names and titles of respect that are part of names.**
  Uncle Frank   Aunt Mary   Governor Adamson
- **Capitalize initials of names.**
  Thomas Paul Gerard (T.P. Gerard)
- **Capitalize place names.**
  France   Utah   China   Baltimore
- **Capitalize *proper adjectives,* adjectives that are made from proper nouns.**
  Chinese   Icelandic   French   Latin American
- **Capitalize the months of the year and the days of the week.**
  February   April   Monday   Tuesday
- **Capitalize important words in the names of products and companies.**
  Blue Brook Cheese Spread   Heart of Gold Applesauce
  Little Hills Bakery   Anderson and Mumford, Inc.
- **Capitalize important words in the names of organizations.**
  American Lung Association   Veterans of Foreign Wars
- **Capitalize important words in the names of holidays.**
  Veterans Day   Fourth of July
- **Capitalize the first word in the greeting or closing of a letter.**
  Dear Edmundo,   Yours truly,
- **Capitalize the word *I*.**
  Frances and I watched the movie together.
- **Capitalize the first, last, and most important words in a title. Be sure to capitalize all verbs including *is* and *was*.**
  Island of the Blue Dolphins
  Away Is a Strange Place to Be
- **Capitalize the first word in a direct quotation.**
  Aunt Rose said, "Please pass the clam dip."

Section 2 Abbreviations and Initials

Abbreviations **are shortened forms of words. Many abbreviations begin with an uppercase letter and end with a period.**

- **You can abbreviate titles of address and titles of respect when you write.**
  Mister (Mr. Brian Davis) Mistress (Mrs. Maria Rosario)
  Doctor (Dr. Emily Chu) Junior (Everett Castle, Jr.)

Note: *Ms.* is a title of address used for women. It is not an abbreviation, but it requires a period (Ms. Anita Brown).

- **You can abbreviate words used in addresses when you write.**
  Street (St.) Avenue (Ave.) Route (Rte.) Boulevard (Blvd.) Road (Rd.)
- **You can abbreviate certain words in the names of businesses when you write.**
  Pet Helpers Incorporated (Pet Helpers Inc.) Zykar Corporation (Zykar Corp.)
- **You can abbreviate days of the week when you take notes.**
  Sunday (Sun.) Wednesday (Wed.) Friday (Fri.)
  Monday (Mon.) Thursday (Thurs.) Saturday (Sat.)
  Tuesday (Tues.)
- **You can abbreviate months of the year when you take notes.**
  January (Jan.) April (Apr.) October (Oct.)
  February (Feb.) August (Aug.) November (Nov.)
  March (Mar.) September (Sept.) December (Dec.)
  (May, June, and July do not have abbreviated forms.)
- **You can abbreviate directions when you take notes.**
  North (N) East (E) South (S) West (W)

An ***initial*** **is the first letter of a name. An initial is written as an uppercase letter and a period. Sometimes initials are used for the names of countries or cities.**

Michael Paul Sanders (M.P. Sanders) United States of America (U.S.A.)
Washington, District of Columbia (Washington, D.C.)

Section 3 Titles

- **Underline titles of books, newspapers, TV series, movies, and magazines.**
  Island of the Blue Dolphins Miami Herald I Love Lucy

Note: These titles are put in italics when using a word processor.

- **Use quotation marks around articles in magazines, short stories, chapters in books, songs, and poems.**
  "This Land Is Your Land" "The Gift" "Eletelephony"
- **Capitalize the first, last, and most important words. Articles, prepositions, and conjunctions are usually not capitalized. Be sure to capitalize all verbs, including forms of the verb** ***be*** **(*****am, is, are, was, were, been*****).**
  A Knight in the Attic *My Brother Sam Is Dead*

Section 4 Quotation Marks

- **Put quotation marks (" ") around the titles of articles, magazines, short stories, book chapters, songs, and poems.**
  My favorite short story is "Revenge of the Reptiles."
- **Put quotation marks around a *direct quotation,* or a speaker's exact words.**
  "Did you see that alligator?" Max asked.
- **Do not put quotation marks around an *indirect quotation,* a person's words retold by another speaker. An indirect quotation is often signalled by *whether* or *that.***
  Max asked Rory whether he had seen an alligator. Rory said that he hadn't.

Writing a Conversation

- **Put quotation marks around the speaker's words. Begin a direct quotation with an uppercase letter. Use a comma to separate the quotation from the speaker's name.**
  Rory said, "There are no alligators in this area."
- **When a direct quotation comes at the end of a sentence, put the end mark inside the last quotation mark.**
  Max cried, "Look out!"
- **When writing a conversation, begin a new paragraph with each change of speaker.**
  Max panted, "I swear I saw a huge, scaly tail and a flat snout in the water!"
  "Relax," Rory said. "I told you there are no alligators around here."

- **Put quotation marks around a quotation from a text.**
  The great civil rights leader Martin Luther King said, "Injustice anywhere is a threat to justice everywhere."

Section 5 Spelling

Use these tips if you are not sure how to spell a word you want to write:

- **Say the word aloud and break it into syllables. Try spelling each syllable. Put the syllables together to spell the whole word.**
- **Write the word. Make sure there is a vowel in every syllable. If the word looks wrong to you, try spelling it other ways.**
- **Think of a related word. Parts of related words are often spelled the same.**
  Decide **is related to** *decision***.**

When you use the word processing function of a computer to write something, you can use the spell-check feature. It will identify possible spelling errors in your writing. A spell checker will not catch errors with homophones, though. For example, if you type *break* instead of *brake,* the spell checker will not catch the mistake, because the word is spelled correctly.

Section 6 End Marks

Every sentence must end with a period, an exclamation point, or a question mark.

- **Use a *period* at the end of a declarative sentence (statement) or an imperative sentence (command).**
  Dad and I look alike. (*declarative*) Step back very slowly. (*imperative*)
- **Use an *exclamation point* at the end of an imperative sentence (a firm command) or at the end of an exclamatory sentence (a sentence that shows great feeling or excitement).**
  Get away from the cliff! (*imperative*) What an incredible sight! (*exclamatory*)
- **Use a *question mark* at the end of an interrogative sentence (question).**
  How many miles is it to Tucson? (*interrogative*)

Section 7 Apostrophes

An apostrophe (') is used to form the possessive of a noun or to join words in a contraction.

- **Possessives show ownership. To make a singular noun possessive, add *'s*.**
  The bike belongs to Carmen. It is Carmen's bike.
  The truck belongs to Mr. Ross. It is Mr. Ross's truck.
- **To form a possessive from a plural noun that ends in *-s,* add only an apostrophe.**
  Those books belong to my sisters. They are my sisters' books.
- **Some plural nouns do not end in *-s.* To form possessives with these nouns, add *'s*.**
  The children left their boots here. The children's boots are wet.
- **Use an apostrophe to replace the dropped letters in a contraction.**
  couldn't (could not) it's (it is) hasn't (has not)
  didn't (did not) I'm (I am) they'll (they will)

Section 8 Commas and Semicolons

Commas in Sentences

- **Use a comma after an introductory word or element in a sentence.**
  Yes, I'd love to go to the movies. Actually, we had a great time.
  Although it was raining, we still had fun at the zoo.
- **Use a comma after a mild interjection at the beginning of a sentence. An *interjection* is a word that expresses emotion but is not part of an independent clause or a dependent clause in a sentence.**
  Oh, it has started raining. Hey, just grab an umbrella!
- **Use a comma to separate items in a series. Put the last comma before *and* or *or*.**
  The puppy whined, scratched at the door, and then barked loudly.
  Shall we eat cheese, bread, or fruit?
- **Use a comma when speaking directly to a person.**
  Akila, will you please stand up? We would like you to sing, Akila.
- **Use a comma to separate a direct quotation from the speaker's name.**
  Harold asked, "How long do I have to sit here?"

"You must sit there until Anton returns," Vic said.

- **Use a comma with the conjunctions *and, or,* and *but* when combining independent clauses in a compound sentence.**
  Lisa liked the reptiles best, but Lyle preferred the amphibians.

Semicolons in Sentences

- **You may use a semicolon in place of a comma and a conjunction when combining independent clauses.**
  Lisa likes reptiles best; Lyle prefers amphibians.

Commas in Letters

- **Use a comma after the greeting and closing of a friendly letter.**
  Dear Reginald, Your friend, Deke

Commas with Dates and Place Names

- **Use a comma to separate the day from the date and the date from the year.**
  We clinched the division championship on Saturday, September 19, 2015.
- **Use a comma to separate the name of a city or town from the name of a state.**
  I visited Memphis, Tennessee.

Sentence Structure and Parts of Speech

Section 9 The Sentence

A *sentence* is a group of words that tells a complete thought. A sentence has two parts: a *subject* and a *predicate*.

- **The subject tells *whom* or *what* the sentence is about.**
  The swimmers race.
- **The predicate tells what the subject *is* or *does*.**
  The judges watch carefully.

There are four kinds of sentences: *declarative, interrogative, imperative,* and *exclamatory*.

- **A sentence that tells something is a *declarative sentence*. It is also called a *statement*. A declarative sentence ends with a period.**
  Jake swam faster than anyone.
- **A sentence that asks something is an *interrogative sentence*. It is also called a *question*. An interrogative sentence ends with a question mark.**
  Did Sammy qualify for the finals?
- **A sentence that tells someone to do something is an *imperative sentence*. It is also called a *command*. An imperative sentence usually ends with a period, but a firm command can end with an exclamation point.**
  Keep your eyes on the finish line.
  Watch out for that bee!
- **A sentence that shows excitement or surprise is called an *exclamation* or *exclamatory sentence*. An exclamation ends with an exclamation point.**
  Jake has won the race!

Section 10 Subjects

The *subject* of a sentence tells whom or what the sentence is about.

- **A sentence can have one subject.**
  Mary wrote a book.
- **A sentence can have a *compound subject*, two or more subjects that share the same predicate.**
  Alex and Mark have already read the book.

The *complete subject* includes all the words that name and tell about the subject.

Many different students have borrowed the book.

The *simple subject* is the most important noun or pronoun in the complete subject.

Many different students have borrowed the book.

They discussed the book yesterday.

Note: Sometimes the simple subject and the complete subject are the same.

Ricardo is writing a book about robots.

Section 11 Predicates

The *predicate* of a sentence tells what happened.

The *complete predicate* includes a verb and all the words that tell what happened.

- A complete predicate can tell what the subject of the sentence did. This kind of predicate includes an action verb.
  Mary won an award.
- A complete predicate can also tell more about the subject. This kind of predicate includes a linking verb.
  Mary is a talented writer.
- A *predicate noun* follows a linking verb and renames the subject.
  Our dog is a retriever.
- A *predicate adjective* follows a linking verb and describes the subject.
  Our dog is friendly.

The *simple predicate* is the verb that goes with the subject. It generally tells what the subject did, does, or will do.

Celia won an award for her performance.

She will receive a trophy next week.

A *compound predicate* is two or more predicates that share the same subject. Compound predicates are often joined by the conjunction *and* or *or*.

Ramon sang and danced in the play.

Mary wrote the play and directed it.

Section 12 Simple, Compound, and Complex Sentences

A sentence expresses one or more complete thoughts.

- A *simple sentence* tells one complete thought.
  Arthur has a rock collection.
- A *compound sentence* is made up of two simple sentences joined by a comma and a coordinating conjunction (*and, or, but*). Two simple sentences can be combined to form one compound sentence if the ideas in the simple sentences are related.
  Arthur has a rock collection, and Mary has a shell collection.
  Arthur collects rocks, but Mary collects shells.
- A *complex sentence* is made up of one *independent clause* (or simple sentence) and at least one dependent clause. A *dependent clause* is a group of words that has a subject and a predicate but cannot stand on its own.
  Dependent Clause: When Arthur visited southern Arizona
  Independent Clause: He learned a lot about desert plants and animals.
  Complex Sentence: When Arthur visited southern Arizona, he learned a lot about desert plants and animals.

Section 13 Fragments, Run-ons, and Comma Splices

A *fragment* is not a sentence, because it is missing a subject or a predicate. A fragment can also be called an incomplete sentence because it does not tell a complete thought.

Sumi and Ali. (*missing a predicate that tells what happened*)
Went hiking in the woods. (*missing a subject that tells who went hiking*)

A *run-on sentence* is two complete sentences that are run together.
Sumi went hiking Ali went swimming.

- **To fix a run-on sentence, use a comma and a conjunction (*and, or, but*) to join the two sentences. (You may also join the sentences with a semicolon.)**
Sumi went hiking<u>, but</u> Ali went swimming.

A *comma splice* is two complete sentences that have a comma between them but are missing a conjunction such as *and, or,* or *but*.
Sumi went hiking yesterday, Ali went swimming.

- **To fix a comma splice, add *and, or,* or *but* after the comma.**
Sumi went hiking yesterday, <u>and</u> Ali went swimming.

Try not to string too many short sentences together when you write. Instead, combine sentences and take out unnecessary information.

Incorrect: I stared at him and he stared at me and I told him to go away and he wouldn't so then I called my big sister.

Correct: We stared at each other. I told him to go away, but he wouldn't. Then I called my big sister.

Section 14 Nouns

A *common noun* names any person, place, thing, or idea.
Ira visited an auto <u>museum</u> with his <u>friends</u>. Ira has always had an <u>interest</u> in <u>cars</u>.

A *proper noun* names a certain person, place, thing, or idea. Proper nouns begin with an uppercase letter.
<u>Ira</u> wants to visit the <u>Sonoran Desert</u> in <u>Mexico</u>.

A *collective noun* names a group of people or things that act as one unit.
jury family committee audience crowd

- **Most often, a collective noun is treated as a singular subject.**
The track <u>team</u> is the strongest one we've had in years.

A *concrete noun* names something you can see, touch, hear, smell, or taste.
dog meadow pebble stove

An *abstract noun* names an idea, a quality, or a characteristic.
freedom bravery freshness excellence

Section 15 Adjectives

An *adjective* is a word that tells more about a noun.

- **Some adjectives tell what kind.**
Jim observed the <u>huge</u> elephant. The <u>enormous</u> beast towered above him.
- **Some adjectives tell how many.**
The elephant was <u>twelve</u> feet tall. It weighed <u>several</u> tons.
- **Sometimes an adjective follows the noun it describes.**
Jim was <u>careful</u> not to anger the elephant. He was <u>happy</u> when the trainer led it away.

- **Two or more adjectives can be used to describe a noun. When you use two or more adjectives to describe a noun, put the adjectives in an order that sounds natural. This chart can help you.**

how many	what quality	how big	how old	what shape	what color	what material	→ noun
three	*beautiful*	*small*	*new*	*round*	*pink*	*silken*	→ petals

- ***A, an,* and *the* are special kinds of adjectives called *articles*. Use *a* and *an* to refer to any person, place, or thing. Use *the* to refer to a specific person, place, or thing. Use *a* before a singular noun that begins with a consonant sound. Use *an* before a singular noun that begins with a vowel sound.**
  An elephant is heavier than a rhino. The elephant in this picture is six weeks old.
- ***Demonstrative adjectives* tell which one. The words *this, that, these,* and *those* can be used as demonstrative adjectives. Use *this* and *these* to talk about things that are nearby. Use *that* and *those* to talk about things that are far away.**
  This book is about rhinos. These rhinos just came to the zoo.
  That rhino is enormous! Those funny-looking creatures are wildebeests.

Note: Never use *here* or *there* after the adjectives *this, that, these,* and *those*.

- **A *proper adjective* is made from a proper noun. Capitalize proper adjectives.**
  Italian cooking Democratic convention Apache legend

Section 16 Pronouns

A *pronoun* can replace a noun naming a person, place, thing, or idea. Personal pronouns include *I, me, you, we, us, he, she, him, her, it, they,* and *them*.

- **A *subject pronoun* takes the place of the subject of a sentence. The subject pronouns are *I, you, he, she, it, we,* and *they*.**
  Rita is an excellent soccer player. She is an excellent soccer player.
- **Do not use both the pronoun and the noun it replaces together.**
  Incorrect: Rita she made the team.
  Correct: Rita made the team. OR She made the team.
- **An *object pronoun* replaces a noun that is the object of a verb or preposition. The object pronouns are *me, you, him, her, it, us,* and *them*.**
  Rita's team played the Bobcats. Rita's team beat them.
- **Use a subject pronoun as part of a compound subject. Use an object pronoun as part of a compound object. To test whether a pronoun is correct, say the sentence without the other part of a compound subject or object.**
  Incorrect: Rita told Ellen and I it was a close game. (Rita told I it was a close game.)
  Correct: Rita told Ellen and me it was a close game. (Rita told me it was a close game.)
- **An *antecedent* is the word or phrase a pronoun refers to. The antecedent always includes a noun.**
  The Bobcats are excellent players. They won every game last season.

- **A pronoun must match its antecedent. An antecedent and a pronoun agree when they have the same *number* (singular or plural) and *gender* (male or female).**
  Nick won the game for our team. He kicked a goal at the last minute.
  Nick's mother cheered. She was very excited.
  The Bobcats were upset. They had not lost a game all season.
- ***Indefinite pronouns* refer to persons or things that are not identified as individuals. These pronouns include *all, anybody, both, anything, few, most, no one,* and *somebody.***
  Somebody lost the key to the gym. We can't do anything unless we find it.
- ***Reflexive pronouns* refer back to the subject of a sentence. A reflexive pronoun contains the word part *self* or *selves.***
  My brother bought himself a new puck. We cheered for ourselves.
- ***This, that, these,* and *those* can be used as demonstrative pronouns. Use *this* and *these* to talk about one or more things that are nearby. Use *that* and *those* to talk about one or more things that are far away.**
  This is a soft rug.
  These are sweeter than those over there.
  That is where I sat yesterday.
  Those are the new chairs I told you about.
- ***Possessive pronouns* show ownership or connection. The words *my, your his, her, its, their,* and *our* are possessive pronouns.**
  Those skates belong to my brother. Those are his kneepads, too.
- **The interrogative pronouns *who, what,* and *which* are used to ask questions.**
  Who has brought the volleyball? What is a wicket used for?
  Which is the net for volleyball?
- **When the pronouns *who, whom, whose, which,* and *that* are used to introduce a dependent clause, they are called *relative pronouns.* A relative pronoun always follows the noun it refers to.**
  The player **who** brought the volleyball can serve first.
  I joined the team **that** chose me.
  This net, **which** I found in my closet, will be perfect for our volleyball game.

Note: For more information on using who, whom, which, and that, see Section 27, Problem Words.

Section 17 Verbs

An *action verb* shows action in a sentence.

Scientists study the natural world. They learn how the laws of nature work.

- **Sometimes a *helping verb* is needed to help the main verb show action. A helping verb comes before a main verb.**
  Scientists are studying glaciers. The studies will help us learn about Earth's history.
- **Verbs can tell about the present, the past, or the future.**
  Few people travel in Antarctica. (*present tense*)
  Explorers first traveled to the South Pole over 100 years ago. (*past tense*)
  Other explorers will travel to the South Pole in the future. (*future tense*)
  Scientists have studied Antarctica for many years. (*present perfect tense*)

Certain helping verbs have special functions. The helping verbs *may* and *might* can be used to ask or give permission. The helping verbs *can* and *could* can be used to indicate ability. The helping verbs *should* and *must* can be used to communicate a duty or an obligation. The helping verbs *may, might, could, should,* and *will* can be used to indicate possibility—how likely something is to happen. Helping verbs that have these special functions are called *modal auxiliaries*.

- **The *present tense* is used to show that something happens regularly or is true now.**
  Squirrels bury nuts each fall.

  Add *-s* to most verbs to show present tense when the subject is *he, she, it,* or a singular noun. Add *-es* to verbs ending in *s, ch, sh,* or *x.* Do not add *-s* or *-es* if the subject is a plural noun or if the subject is *I, you, we,* or *they.*

add *-s*	**add *-es***	**change *y* to *i* and add *-es***
speak/speaks	reach/reaches	carry/carries
look/looks	mix/mixes	bury/buries

- **The *past tense* shows past action. Add *-ed* to most verbs to form the past tense. Verbs that do not add *-ed* are called *irregular verbs.* Here are some common irregular verbs.**

Present	**Past**	**With *has, have,* or *had***
blow	blew	blown
bring	brought	brought
catch	caught	caught
come	came	come
find	found	found
give	gave	given
go	went	gone
grow	grew	grown
hide	hid	hidden
know	knew	known
leave	left	left
set	set	set
sing	sang	sung
sit	sat	sat
sleep	slept	slept
take	took	taken
teach	taught	taught
tell	told	told
throw	threw	thrown

- **The future tense indicates future action. Use the helping verb *will* to form the future tense.**
  Mom will visit Antarctica next year. She will photograph penguins.

- **Perfect-tense verbs are used to indicate certain time relationships.**

  The *present perfect tense* shows action that began in the past and may still be happening. To form the present perfect tense, add the helping verb *has* or *have* to the past participle of a verb.
  Mom has studied Antarctica for years. Her articles have appeared in science journals.

  The *past perfect tense* shows action that was completed by a certain time in the past. To form the past perfect tense, add the helping verb *had* to the past participle of a verb.
  Before she visited Antarctica, Mom had imagined it as a wasteland.

  The *future perfect tense* shows action that will be complete by a certain time in the future. To form the future perfect tense, add the helping verbs *will have* to the past participle form of a verb.
  By the end of the year, Mom will have published a book on Antarctic sea creatures.

- **The subject and its verb must agree in number.**
  An Antarctic explorer needs special equipment.
  (*singular subject:* **An Antarctic explorer;** *verb + -s or -es:* **needs**)
  Explorers carry climbing tools and survival gear.
  (*plural subject:* **Explorers;** *verb without -s or -es:* **carry**)

A *linking verb* does not show action. It connects the subject of a sentence to a word or words in the predicate that tell about the subject. Linking verbs include forms of the verb *be,* such as *am, is, are, was,* and *were. Seem* and *become* are linking verbs, too.

Explorers are brave. That route seems very long and dangerous.

Note: *Feel, taste, smell, sound,* and *look* can be action or linking verbs.

- **Choose verb tenses carefully so that the verb forms you use work together to indicate time accurately and consistently. When you describe events that happen in the same time frame, do not shift tenses. When you describe events that happen at different times, use verbs in different tenses to indicate the order in which the events happened.**
  Malcolm wanted to stay dry on the hike, so he packed a poncho. (not packs)
  The doves begin their calls early in the morning, and they continue them past noon. (not continued)

Section 18 Adverbs

An *adverb* is usually used to describe a verb or an adjective. Most adverbs tell how, when, where, or how much.

- **Many adverbs end in *-ly*.**
  Andrew approached the snake cage slowly. He cautiously peered inside.
- **Some adverbs do not end in *-ly*.**
  Andrew knew that snakes can move fast.
- ***Very* is an adverb. It means "extremely." Never use *real* in place of *very*.**

Incorrect	**Correct**
The snake's fangs were real sharp.	The snake's fangs were very sharp.

- **When the word *when, where,* or *why* begins a dependent clause that tells about a**

place, a time, or a reason, it can be called a *relative adverb.*

Tucker Avenue is a street <u>where</u> many accidents happen. (place)

Friday is the day <u>when</u> my report is due. (time)

This article gives five reasons <u>why</u> you should drink water instead of soda. (reason)

Note: A word that is a relative adverb can also be classified as a subordinating conjunction.

Section 19 Prepositions

A *preposition* shows a relationship between a word in a sentence and a noun or pronoun that follows the preposition. Prepositions help tell when, where, what kind, how, or how much.

- **Prepositions include the words *in, at, under, over, on, through, to, across, around, beside, during, off,* and *before.***

  Jeff left the milk <u>on</u> the table. He knew it belonged <u>in</u> the refrigerator.

- **A *prepositional phrase* is a group of words that begins with a preposition and ends with its object. The object of a preposition is a noun or a pronoun. A prepositional phrase can be at the beginning, middle, or end of a sentence.**

  Jeff knew his mother would be home <u>in five minutes</u>.

  <u>Within three minutes</u> Jeff had put the milk away.

The *object of a preposition* is the noun or pronoun at the end of a prepositional phrase.

Milt gave a pen to his <u>sister</u>. (*Sister* is the object of the preposition *to*.)

Section 20 Direct Objects and Indirect Objects

A *direct object* is the word or words that receive the action of the verb. Direct objects follow action verbs. (A linking verb never has a direct object.) To find the direct object, say the verb followed by "Whom?" or "What?" A direct object is always a noun or pronoun.

Jacques painted a <u>picture.</u> (Painted whom or what? Picture. *Picture* is the direct object.)

A sentence with a direct object may also have an *indirect object*. An indirect object is a noun or pronoun and usually tells to whom something is given.

Jacques gave his <u>mom</u> the painting.

Section 21 Conjunctions

The words *and, or,* and *but* are *coordinating conjunctions.* They connect words or groups of words that have the same function.

- **Coordinating conjunctions may be used to join words within a sentence.**

  My favorite reptiles are snakes <u>and</u> lizards. Najim doesn't like snakes <u>or</u> lizards.

- **A comma and a coordinating conjunction can be used to join two or more simple sentences. (The conjunction *and* does not need a comma if both sentences are short.)**

  I like snakes, <u>but</u> he says they're creepy. We can get a snake, <u>or</u> we can get a lizard.

A *subordinating conjunction* shows how one clause (a group of words with a subject and predicate) relates to another clause. Many dependent clauses begin with a subordinating conjunction. Subordinating conjunctions include *although, because, if,* and *before.*

Before his mom left, Bo cleaned his room. **Because** he had a favor to ask, he vacuumed, too.

Correlative conjunctions* always appear in pairs. They connect words or groups of words and provide more emphasis than coordinating conjunctions. Some correlative conjunctions are *both…and, either…or, neither…nor, not only…but (also),* and *whether…or.

You can **either** wash the car **or** mow the lawn.
Emma is using **both** the broom **and** the vacuum cleaner.

Usage

Section 22 Negatives

A *negative word* says "no" or "not."

- **Often negatives are in the form of contractions.**
  Do <u>not</u> enter that room. <u>Don't</u> even go near the door.
- **In most sentences it is not correct to use two negatives.**

Incorrect	Correct
We <u>can't</u> see <u>nothing</u>.	We <u>can't</u> see anything.
We <u>haven't</u> got <u>no</u> solution.	We <u>haven't</u> got a solution.

- **Do not use the word *ain't*.**

Section 23 Comparisons

- **The *comparative form* of an adjective or adverb compares two people, places, or things. The comparative form is often followed by "than." To compare two people, places, or things, add *-er* to short adjectives and adverbs.**
  An elephant is <u>tall</u>. A giraffe is <u>taller</u> than an elephant. (*Giraffe* is compared with *elephant*.)

  A lion runs <u>fast</u>. A cheetah runs <u>faster</u> than any other land animal. (*Cheetah* is compared with *any other land animal.*)
- **The *superlative form* of an adjective or adverb compares three or more people, places, or things. The article "the" usually comes before the superlative form. To compare three or more items, add *-est* to short adjectives and adverbs.**
  The giraffe is the <u>tallest</u> land animal.

  The cheetah runs the <u>fastest</u> of any animal now alive.
- **When comparing two or more things using the ending *-er* or *-est,* never use the word *more*.**

Incorrect	Correct
She is <u>more faster</u> than he is.	She is <u>faster</u> than he is.

- **The word *more* is used with longer adjectives to compare two persons, places, or things. Use the word *most* to compare three or more persons, places, or things.**
  Mario is <u>excited</u> about the field trip.

  Duane is <u>more excited</u> than Mario.

  Kiki is the <u>most excited</u> student of all.
- **Sometimes the words *good* and *bad* are used to compare. These words change forms in comparisons.**

Mario is a <u>good</u> athlete.	The basketball court is in <u>bad</u> shape.
Kiki is a <u>better</u> athlete.	The tennis court is in <u>worse</u> shape than the basketball court.
Bill is the <u>best</u> athlete of all.	The ice rink is in the <u>worst</u> shape of all.

Note: Use *better* or *worse* to compare two things. Use *best* or *worst* to compare three or more things.

Section 24 Contractions

When two or more words are combined to form one word, one or more letters are dropped and replaced by an apostrophe. These words are called *contractions.*

- **In the contraction below, an apostrophe takes the place of the letters *wi*.**
  he will = he'll
- **Here are some other common contractions.**

cannot/can't	have not/haven't	she would/she'd
could not/couldn't	I will/I'll	they have/they've
does not/doesn't	it is/it's	we are/we're

Section 25 Plural Nouns

- **A *singular noun* names one person, place, thing, or idea.**
  girl pond arrow freedom
- **A *plural noun* names more than one person, place, or thing. To make most singular nouns plural, add *-s*.**
  girls ponds arrows freedoms
- **For nouns ending in *sh, ch, x,* or *z,* add *-es* to make the word plural.**
  bush/bushes box/boxes
  lunch/lunches buzz/buzzes
- **For nouns ending in a consonant and *y,* change the *y* to *i* and add *-es*.**
  penny/pennies army/armies
- **For nouns that end in *f* or *fe,* replace *f* or *fe* with *ves* to make the noun plural.**
  shelf/shelves wife/wives
- **Some words change spelling when the plural is formed.**
  man/men woman/women mouse/mice goose/geese
- **Some words have the same singular and plural form.**
  deer sheep

Section 26 Possessive Nouns

A ***possessive noun*** **shows ownership.**

- **To make a singular noun possessive, add an apostrophe and *-s*.**
  John's bat the girl's bike
- **When a singular noun ends in *-s,* add an apostrophe and *-s*.**
  Ross's project James's glasses
- **To make a plural noun that ends in *-s* possessive, add an apostrophe.**
  the soldiers' songs the girls' bikes
- **When a plural noun does not end in *-s,* add an apostrophe and *s* to show possession.**
  the men's ideas the children's shoes

Section 27 Problem Words

These words are often misused in writing.

sit	***Sit* means "rest or stay in one place."** Sit down and relax for a while.
sat	***Sat* is the past tense of *sit*.** I sat in that chair yesterday.
set	***Set* is a verb meaning "put."** Set the chair here.
may	***May* is used to ask permission or to express a possibility.** May I have another hot dog? I may borrow that book someday.
can	***Can* shows that someone is able to do something.** I can easily eat three hot dogs.
learn	***Learn* means "to get knowledge."** Who will help you learn Spanish?
teach	***Teach* means "to give knowledge." Never use *learn* in place of *teach*.** **Incorrect:** My sister will learn me to speak Spanish. **Correct:** My sister will teach me to speak Spanish.
is	**Use *is* to tell about one person, place, or thing.** Alabama is warm during the summer.
are	**Use *are* to tell about more than one person, place, or thing. Also use *are* with the word *you*.** Seattle and San Francisco are cool during the summer. You are welcome to visit me anytime.
doesn't	**The contraction *doesn't* is used with the singular pronouns *he, she,* and *it*.** He doesn't like sauerkraut. It doesn't agree with him.
don't	**The contraction *don't* is used with the plural pronouns *we* and *they*. *Don't* is also used with *I* and *you*.** They don't like swiss cheese. I don't care for it, either.
I	**Use the pronoun *I* as the subject of a sentence. When using *I* or *me* with another noun or pronoun, always name yourself last.** I am going to basketball camp. Renée and I will ride together.
me	**Use the pronoun *me* after action verbs.** Renée will call me this evening. **Also use *me* after a preposition, such as *to, at,* and *with*.** Pass the ball to me. Come to the game with Renée and me.
good well	***Good* is an adjective.** ***Well* is an adverb. These words are often used incorrectly.** **Incorrect:** Renée plays good. **Correct:** Renée is a good basketball player. She plays well.

like	***Like*** **means "similar to" or "have a fondness for." Do not use** ***like*** **in places where it does not belong.** **Incorrect:** I enjoy, like, all kinds of water sports. **Correct:** I like swimming and water polo.
you know	**Only use the phrase** ***you know*** **when it helps a sentence make sense. Try not to use it in places where it does not belong.** **Incorrect:** We can, you know, go canoeing. **Correct:** Did you know that my family has a canoe?
let	***Let*** **is a verb that means "allow."** Please let me go to the mall with you.
leave	***Leave*** **is a verb that means "go away from" or "let stay."** We will leave at noon. Leave your sweater here.
was	***Was*** **is a past tense form of** ***be*****. Use** ***was*** **to tell about one person or thing.** Hana was sad yesterday.
were	***Were*** **is also a past tense form of** ***be*****. Use** ***were*** **to tell about more than one person or thing. Also use the word** ***were*** **with** ***you*****.** Hana and her friend were both unhappy. Were you home yesterday?
has	**Use** ***has*** **to tell about one person or thing.** Rory has a stamp collection.
have	**Use** ***have*** **to tell about more than one. Also use** ***have*** **with the pronoun** ***I*****.** David and Lin have a rock collection. I have a bottle cap collection.
who	**Use** ***who*** **to refer to people.** The man who picked me up is my father.
which	**Use** ***which*** **to refer to things.** His rear tire, which was flat, had to be repaired.
that	***That*** **can refer to people or things. Use** ***that*** **instead of** ***which*** **to begin a clause that is necessary to the meaning of the sentence.** The picture that Stephon drew won first prize.
very	***Very*** **is an adverb. It means "extremely."** I was very tired after the hike.
real	***Real*** **is an adjective. It means "actual" or "true to life." Never use** ***real*** **in place of** ***very*****.** **Incorrect:** The hike was real long. **Correct:** I used a real compass to find my way.

Section 28 Homophones

Homophones sound alike but have different spellings and meanings.

are	***Are* is a form of the verb *be*.**	We are best friends.
our	***Our* is a possessive pronoun.**	Our favorite color is green.
hour	**An *hour* is sixty minutes.**	Meet me in an hour.
its	***Its* is a possessive pronoun.**	The horse shook its shaggy head.
it's	***It's* is a contraction of the words *it is*.**	It's a beautiful day for a ride.
there	***There* is an adverb that usually means "in that place." It can also be used in the expressions "there is" and "there are."** Please put the books there. There is a library nearby.	There are three books on the table.
their	***Their* is a possessive pronoun. It shows something belongs to more than one person or thing.** Their tickets are in my pocket.	
they're	***They're* is a contraction made from the words *they are*.** They're waiting for me inside.	
two	***Two* is a number.**	Apples and pears are two fruits I like.
to	***To* means "toward."**	I brought the pot to the stove.
too	***Too* means "also."**	I'd like some lunch, too.
	***Too* can mean "more than enough."**	That's too much pepper!
your	***Your* is a possessive pronoun.** Where are your socks?	
you're	***You're* is a contraction made from the words *you are*.** You're coming with us, aren't you?	
whose	***Whose* is a possessive pronoun.** Whose raincoat is this?	
who's	***Who's* is a contraction made from the words *who* and *is* or *who* and *has*.** Who's at the front door?	Who's taken my book?
ate	***Ate* is a form of the verb *eat*.**	We ate lunch together.
eight	***Eight* is a number word.**	She had eight marbles.
principal	**A *principal* is a person with authority.** The principal made the rule.	
principle	**A *principle* is a general rule or code of behavior.** He lived with a strong principle of honesty.	
waist	**The *waist* is the middle part of the body.** She wore a belt around her waist.	
waste	**To *waste* something is to use it in a careless way.** She would never waste something she could recycle.	
aloud	***Aloud* means "out loud" or "able to be heard."** He read the poem aloud.	
allowed	***Allowed* is a form of the verb *allow*.** We were not allowed to swim after dark.	

Letters and E-mails

Section 29 Letters

A *friendly letter* is an informal letter written to a friend or family member. In a friendly letter, you might send a message, invite someone to a party, or thank someone for a gift. A friendly letter has five parts.

- The *heading* gives your address and the date.
- The *greeting* includes the name of the person you are writing to.
- The *body* of the letter gives your message.
- The *closing* is a friendly or polite way to say good-bye.
- The *signature* is your name.

> 35 Rand Street
> Chicago, IL 60606
> July 15, 20__
>
> Dear Kim,
>
> Hi from the big city. I'm spending the summer learning to skateboard. My brother Raj is teaching me. He's a pro.
>
> I have one skateboard and hope to buy another one soon. If I can do that, we can practice together when you come to visit.
>
> Your friend,
>
> Art

A *business letter* is a formal letter. You would write a business letter to a company, an employer, a newspaper, or any person you do not know well. A business letter looks a lot like a friendly letter, but it also includes the name and address of the business you are writing to, substitutes a colon for a comma after the greeting, omits paragraph indentations, and aligns all of the letter parts along the left-hand margin.

> 35 Rand Street
> Chicago, IL 60606
> July 15, 20__
>
> Swenson Skateboard Company
> 10026 Portage Road
> Lansing, MI 48091
>
> Dear Sir or Madam:
>
> Please send me your latest skateboard catalog. I am particularly interested in your newest models, the K-7 series.
>
> Thank you.
>
> Sincerely yours,
> Arthur Quinn
> Arthur Quinn

The envelope below shows how to address a letter. A friendly letter and a business letter are addressed the same way.

> ARTHUR QUINN
> 35 RAND ST
> CHICAGO IL 60606
>
> KIM LEE
> 1555 MONTAGUE BLVD
> MEMPHIS TN 38106

Section 30 E-mails

An *e-mail* is a note sent from one person to another person, a group, or a company via a computer network. Many people use e-mail to stay in touch with friends and family. An e-mail should contain four parts.

- An e-mail contains a *greeting,* a *body,* a *closing,* and your *name.*
- An e-mail *header* contains your e-mail address, the e-mail address of the person you are writing to, the date, and a subject line.

Send | Save as a Draft | Cancel

From: arthur_quinn@communicago.net

To: info@swenskate.com

Date: July 15, 20__

Subject: Skateboard catalog

Attach Files

Dear Sir or Madam:

Please send me your latest skateboard catalog. I am particularly interested in your newest models, the K-7 series.

My address is 35 Rand Street, Chicago, IL 60606. Thank you.

Sincerely,
Arthur Quinn

Research

Section 31 Library Research

You can find information for a report or a project in a library.

- Many libraries have an information desk. The person at the desk can help you look for information.
- Libraries have many reference books, including dictionaries, thesauruses, and encyclopedias. You can use these to find information about words, and basic information about topics.
- Libraries have nonfiction books about all kinds of subjects. You can find books on a particular subject by entering that subject into a computer connected to the library's database. This database lists all the publications in the library. The computer will usually list several books on the subject you entered. Each listing will have a code that tells where in the library that book can be found.

Section 32 Internet Research

You can use online dictionaries, thesauruses, and encyclopedias to find basic information about words and topics. You can also find information for a report or a project by using an Internet *search engine*.

- Think of **key words** that tell what you are looking for. For example, if you need information on animals that live in the rain forest, you might use the key words **rain forest animals.** Type these words into the search engine's text box.
- The search engine will provide you with links to **websites.** You can click on a link to visit a website.
- When you get to the website, you need to judge whether it will be a good source of information.
  — Notice the last three letters of the website's Internet address. Sites with a **.gov** and **.edu** are usually more reliable than sites with **.com.**
  — Think about who has written the information. Is the writer an expert on the topic? Is the writer giving facts, or just expressing opinions?
  — Check to see if the information is up-to-date. The site should tell you when it was last updated.

Internet Safety

Be sure to follow safety rules whenever you use the Internet. These rules will help you keep personal information private.

- When you log on to a school computer, you may type your own name as a username. However, when you go on the Internet, you use a screen name. That should never be your real name or nickname. You will also use a password, a secret word or symbol that identifies who you are. Keep your password safe. Do not share it with anyone. Never use your address, birthday, phone number, or pet's name as a password. Those are too easy for someone else to figure out.
- Have you ever received e-mail with an attachment? Usually you must click the attachment to load it into your computer. Never download attachments from strangers. These may harm your computer.

Guidelines for Listening and Speaking

Section 33 Listening

These steps will help you be a good listener:

- **Listen carefully** when others are speaking.
- **Keep in mind your reason for listening.** Are you listening to learn about a topic? To be entertained? To get directions? Decide what you should get out of the listening experience.
- **Look directly at the speaker.** Doing this will help you concentrate on what he or she has to say.
- **Do not interrupt** the speaker or talk to others while the speaker is talking.
- **Ask questions** when the speaker is finished talking if there is anything you did not understand.

Section 34 Speaking

Being a good speaker takes practice. These guidelines can help you become an effective speaker:

Giving Oral Reports

- **Be prepared.** Know exactly what it is that you are going to talk about and how long you will speak. Have your notes in front of you.
- **Speak slowly** and **clearly.** Speak **loudly** enough so everyone can hear you.
- **Look** at your audience.

Taking Part in Discussions

- **Listen** to what others have to say.
- **Disagree politely.** Let others in the group know you respect their point of view.
- **Try not to interrupt others.** Everyone should have a chance to speak.

Language Index

Conventions of Standard English